QUEENSW
INTELLIGENCE
TESTS

Metricated Edition

UNWIN HYMAN

Published by
UNWIN HYMAN LIMITED
15-17 Broadwick Street
London W1V 1FP

© Unwin Hyman Limited 1983
First published in 1959 by Evans Brothers Limited
New edition 1970
Reprinted by Unwin Hyman Limited 1986, 1988

ISBN 0 7135 1485 X

Printed in Great Britain by
Thetford Press Limited, Thetford, Norfolk

FOREWORD

THE ability of children to tackle Intelligence Tests successfully is like all the other abilities that find expression in school work; it can be given adequate opportunities for its exercise, or denied them, and the result will be either that we shall be provided with test-scores that can be relied on to supply us with reliable evidence of the mental powers of the children responsible for them, or evidence which it would be unwise to accept without question.

When Intelligence Tests were first introduced into the schools it was widely believed that they would give us genuine measures of the inborn ability of our pupils, independent of, and uninfluenced by, any kind of training or environmental effect. It would be nothing short of a miracle, however, if the maxim " Practice makes perfect " applied to every variety of school performance except that represented by an Intelligence Test score, and certainly no teacher expects miracles to happen in the classroom.

There are many good reasons for refusing to allow the claims made by the more extreme of those psychologists who advocate the universal use of these tests for measuring human ability. In the first place, the kind of intelligence tests employed in classifying children according to their general mental powers is usually one which is couched in verbal form, consisting, that is, of questions presented in print, and entailing, therefore, the possession of a certain degree of skill in reading if they are to be dealt with satisfactorily. We all know, of course, that this skill is not come by, in the majority of cases, except at the cost of considerable labour on the part of teachers as well as of pupils. This means that those children who have enjoyed the experience of being taught by an exceptional teacher and those who are backward on account of absence from school at critical times in their lives cannot be expected to put up performances in an Intelligence Test which are commensurate with their abilities; those of the former will be the product of ability plus teaching skill, those of the latter will be the product of ability labouring under a more or less severe handicap which they may be unable to overcome. We know, too, that schools vary a great deal in tone and spirit and the test-performances of children must depend to some extent on the working habits they acquire in the school to which they have been admitted. In one school they will learn to put their best efforts into everything they do, concentrating on the task in hand without strain, and producing results that are a faithful indication of their mental capacity, whereas in another school with an easier and slower tempo of life they will never quite succeed in learning to bring to bear all the potential ability within them upon the work required because too little in the way of disciplined long-term effort has been expected from them.

It is in the light of facts of this kind that the question of coaching must be considered. What is attempted in coaching is, first of all, to train children to use their powers to the full and, second, to familiarise them with the nature of such tasks as they may be judged by when the occasion arises. Clearly, it is impossible to go beyond Nature's limit in getting children to bring to bear whatever powers they possess on a given task. All that we can say is that the livelier and richer their experience the more likely they are to develop the confidence and skill needed to show themselves to advantage so that to depend entirely on teaching them the tricks of test-performance will be extremely bad policy.

Nevertheless, it is unfair to children to deprive them of the opportunity of becoming acquainted with the type of test by which their fitness for a particular form of education will be decided. In the past some children have had the advantage of skilful preparation for their primary school leaving examination while others have not been so fortunate. The present handbook will enable the parents and teachers of the less fortunate children to make good what has been missed.

An Intelligence Test of the type usually given to children in examinations takes from 40 to 50 minutes for the ablest of them to complete. Each of the exercises in this handbook should take about 10 minutes. But it is less important to aim at speed than at thoughtful effort. Errors made should be fully discussed in a sympathetic and helpful spirit. What must ever be remembered is that the anxiety from which children suffer in advance of, and during their examination ordeal, is mostly caught from parents and teachers who cannot refrain from treating them as the instruments of their own ambitions.

CONTENTS

I. UNDERSTANDING INSTRUCTIONS

Example

A B C D E F G H I J K L M N O P Q R S T U V W X Y Z

1. Which is the 13th letter in the alphabet ?
   The answer is M.
2. Which letter is the 13th from the end counting backwards ?
   The answer is N.

EXERCISE 1a

1. Write down the fifth letter of the alphabet.
2. Write down the fourth letter after O.
3. Counting backwards, write down the fifth letter from the end of the alphabet.
4. Which is the third letter after the second letter before C ?
5. Write down the letter that comes halfway between A and E.
6. Write down the letter that comes halfway between F and L.
7. If the third and fifth letters of the alphabet were missing, what would be the seventh letter ?
8. Write down the letter that comes halfway between I and O.
9. Write down the letter that comes after the letter that is the third letter after S.
10. Which two letters of the alphabet, taken together, have the same number of letters before them as after them ?
11. Which letter occurs oftenest in COSMOPOLITAN ?
12. Which letter occurs oftenest in EYESORES ?
13. Which letter comes most often in INDEFINITE ?
14. Which letter is found in SUNDAYS but not in MONDAYS ?
15. Which letter in the word EXERCISE comes just before the last of the three letters that are the same ?
16. Write down the name of the second of the three months that end in -EMBER.
17. Write down the first letter of the month that has the longest name.
18. Write down backwards the name of the month that has the shortest name.
19. Which day of the week has most letters in its name ?
20. Which is the eighth month of the year ?

21. Take the even number next above 6 from the odd number next below 12.

22. Think of the numbers between 12 and 18 and write down the middle one.

23. Write down the middle even number between 11 and 21.

24. If 7 is the half of 14 write R, if not, write W.

25. Divide the largest number in the next line by the smallest :
    16, 18, 9, 28, 56, 39, 42, 8, 12.

26. Take the smallest odd number from the largest even number :
    42, 15, 27, 14, 32, 51, 24.

27. Add together all the odd numbers between 1 and 10.

28. Add together all the even numbers between 1 and 10.

29. Add 3, 5 and 7 together. If the answer is more than 12 print the answer as a *word*. If it is less than 12 print the answer as a *figure*.

30. Write down the tens figures of the following numbers in the order in which they come : 36, 29, 83 and 15.

EXERCISE 1b

Copy the first drawing.

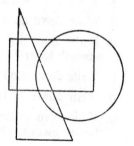

1. Put 6 in the space which is in both the triangle and the circle but not in the rectangle.

2. Put 7 in the space which is in both the triangle and the rectangle but not in the circle.

3. Put 8 in the space which is in the rectangle and the circle but not in the triangle.

4. Put X in the space which is in the circle and in the triangle and in the rectangle.

Copy the second drawing.

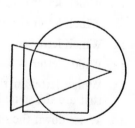

5. Put A in the space which is in the circle but not in the square or the triangle.

6. Put B in the space which is in the triangle but not in the square or the circle.

7. Put C in the space which is in the square but not in the triangle or the circle.

8. Put D in the space which is in the square and the triangle but not in the circle.

9. Put E in the space which is in the square and the circle but not in the triangle.

10. Put F in the space which is in the circle and the triangle but not in the square.

2. FINDING SIMILAR MEANINGS
EXERCISE 2a

Look at each word in Capital Letters and write out one of the four words following it that has the same or nearly the same meaning.

Example

    HEAVY   light, dark, <u>weighty,</u> big.

The correct word is underlined for you.

1. LARGE   small, size, big, barge.
2. WEAK   strong, feeble, tired, little.
3. DAMP   moist, warm, cold, icy.
4. DEAR   nice, cheap, comfortable, expensive.
5. MASTER   governor, servant, mistress, doctor.
6. WEALTHY   healthy, wise, rich, generous.
7. COMING   going, proceeding, journeying, approaching.
8. SHARP   acute, knife, razor, saucy.
9. OFTEN   seldom, frequently, rarely, always.
10. FIGHT   enemy, foe, combat, force.
11. POWERFUL   rich, mighty, proud, severe.
12. PASSAGE   room, hall, cloakroom, corridor.
13. PECULIAR   strange, silly, foolish, fussy.
14. PERMANENT   temporary, usual, lasting, remaining.
15. COURAGEOUS   encouraging, cowardly, sensible, brave.
16. LOATHE   love, cherish, detest, denounce.
17. TERRIFY   unearth, terrible, frighten, bury.
18. OPAQUE   obscure, fixed, transparent, transmitting.
19. AMIABLE   good-natured, feeble, foolish, proud.
20. DEDUCT   infer, subtract, extract, reduce.
21. GRATITUDE   greatness, meanness, sufficiency, thankfulness.
22. ENTHUSIASM   excitement, zeal, fuss, success.
23. ANXIETY   carefulness, unpleasantness, determination, distress.
24. APPRECIATION   prayer, comfort, approval, dislike.

25. ELEGANCE	grace, display, safety, election.
26. TOLERANCE	forbearance, weight, approbation, regard.
27. EXTRAVAGANCE	extraction, economy, waste, vagrancy.
28. PRUDENCE	interference, proof, caution, affection.
29. SURPRISE	satisfaction, astonishment, disappointment, shame.
30. REPUTATION	calculation, reference, memory, character.

EXERCISE 2b

In the following sentences you will see that some words are *in italics*. Four words follow each sentence. One of these has the same (or nearly the same) meaning as the word *in italics*. Write down the word you think has the same (or nearly the same) meaning as the word *in italics* in the sentence.

1. I bought a pane of *clear* glass.
   distinct, transparent, frosted, tinted.

2. An *accurate* answer is required.
   correct, clear, neat, tidy.

3. Uncle John was a *melancholy* man.
   mean, surly, sad, poor.

4. He was in receipt of a *substantial* income.
   firm, considerable, uncertain, meagre.

5. The package had been plainly marked *fragile*.
   light, careful, brittle, thin.

6. The error was of no great *significance*.
   handwriting, reality, importance, result.

7. The majority of the people were *illiterate*.
   careless, stupid, unable to speak, unable to read.

8. A child's birthday is an *annual* occurrence.
   usual, yearly, exciting, happy.

9. A metal bar will *contract* in very cold weather.
   break, freeze, lengthen, shorten.

10. What *folly* to think that things will improve.
    stupidity, insight, wisdom, news.

EXERCISE 2c

Look at the figures at the beginning of each line. Can you match them by another set that comes later in the same line ? Write the number of item you choose.

Example

$6 \times 6 =$ (1) $12 + 12$ (2) 8×4 (3) $72 \div 9$ (4) 12×3.
The answer is (4) $12 \times 3 = 36$, just as $6 \times 6 = 36$.

		(1)	(2)	(3)	(4)
1.	$3 \times 4 =$	8×2	4×2	2×6	$3 + 4$
2.	$8 + 7 =$	$20 \div 4$	5×3	$18 - 5$	7×8
3.	$24 - 6 =$	$8 + 8$	6×4	$9 + 9$	$24 \div 2$
4.	$36 \div 3 =$	$17 - 5$	4×9	$12 + 6$	$12 + 12$
5.	$50 + 50 =$	$100 \div 2$	$100 + 2$	$100 - 0$	50×1

EXERCISE 2d

Find the right answer (a, b, c or d) for each statement below.

1. *Make hay while the sun shines,* means :
   (a) Don't try to make hay in wet weather.
   (b) Use your chance while you can.
   (c) Enjoy the good weather while it lasts.
   (d) Work while it is sunny ; rest while it is cloudy.

2. *Look before you leap,* means :
   (a) Think before you act.
   (b) Try not to bump into people in the street.
   (c) Don't jump into water ; step in.
   (d) Look right and left before crossing the road.

3. *All is not gold that glitters,* means :
   (a) Gold does not glitter all over.
   (b) Silver glitters as well as gold.
   (c) Diamonds glitter even more.
   (d) You cannot always judge by appearances.

4. *Too many cooks spoil the broth,* means :
   (a) To get good broth you need only a few cooks.
   (b) One person is usually wiser than many persons.
   (c) You must not allow interference when a plan is going well.
   (d) Many hands make light work.

3. WORDS OPPOSITE IN MEANING

Many of the words in our language can be written down in pairs, one of which is opposite in meaning to the other. Here are some examples : **up, down ; in, out ; back, front.** Some children think of words that often come together as opposites when they really are not : for example, **pen** and **ink, cat** and **dog** are not opposites. Many words form their own opposites by taking what is called a prefix like **un-** or **dis-.** So we have **pleasant** and **unpleasant ; agreeable** and **disagreeable.**

Let us begin with an easy exercise.

EXERCISE 3a

Look at the words in capital letters. Write out one of the five words which is opposite in meaning to the word in capitals.

1. ABOVE :   over, below, high, lofty, cloudy.
2. FAT :   fair, fleshy, thin, bulky, tasty.
3. SHARP :   clever, blunt, keen, even, eager.
4. NEAR :   far, mean, here, close, there.
5. SAINT :   priest, monk, nun, hermit, sinner.
6. WEAK :   ailing, day, strong, feeble, handsome.
7. SMOOTH :   pleasant, shiny, gentle, rough, plain.
8. FOLLOW :   imitate, lead, accompany, excel, succeed.
9. REMEMBER : memorise, repeat, recall, forget, retrieve.
10. PEACE :   quietness, war, silence, portion, treaty.

EXERCISE 3b

There are five words in every one of the ten lines below. Find two words in each line that have opposite meanings.

1. Gentle, breezy, violent, unselfish, broad.
2. Despatch, destroy, upset, construct, distribute.
3. Pretty, innocent, unfair, guilty, wise.
4. Give, inquire, except, deceive, receive.
5. Exit, extricate, accept, entrance, entire.
6. Grey, important, insignificant, intricate, complex.
7. Cosmetic, costly, outrageous, inexpensive, charming.
8. Clever, tall, energetic, handsome, lazy.
9. Display, charm, work, conceal, sell.
10. Measure, dispatch, diminish, infest, increase.

EXERCISE 3c

Example

COME is the opposite of—which?

(1) wait   (2) stand   (3) sit   (4) go   (5) full

The answer is GO. Find the word that is the opposite (or very nearly the opposite) of the word in capitals at the beginning and write down the number that goes with it.

1. FRIEND :   (1) lover   (2) relative   (3) foe   (4) ally   (5) helper
2. SORROW :   (1) fear   (2) joy   (3) grief   (4) anger   (5) mourning
3. BRIEF :   (1) short   (2) fat   (3) lengthy   (4) curtailed (5) medium
4. HIDE :   (1) uncover   (2) conceal   (3) disguise   (4) seek   (5) run
5. ABSURD :   (1) deaf   (2) silly   (3) sensible   (4) foolish   (5) clear
6. IMPROVE :   (1) increase   (2) prove   (3) discover   (4) spoil   (5) mend
7. RESOLVE :   (1) hesitate   (2) decide   (3) search   (4) turn   (5) insist
8. PERPETUAL : (1) endless   (2) momentary (3) forward   (4) timely   (5) perfect
9. DESCEND :   (1) rise   (2) sink   (3) crouch   (4) hurry   (5) proceed
10. EXTERIOR :   (1) outside   (2) external   (3) inside   (4) infernal   (5) casement

EXERCISE 3d

Look at each pair of words below. Are they the <u>same</u> in meaning, <u>opposite</u> in meaning or are they <u>neither</u> the same nor the opposite? Write S (for <u>same</u>), O (for <u>opposite</u>) or N (for <u>neither</u>) to show what the answer should be.

Example   summit, top   (s)

1.	Agree	Differ	6.	Purple	Orange
2.	Danger	Safety	7.	Buttercup	Daisy
3.	Many	Numerous	8.	Eloquent	Speechless
4.	Rare	Uncommon	9.	Delicious	Appetising
5.	Blend	Mingle	10.	Cheese	Butter

EXERCISE 3e

Look at the words in capital letters below. Each is followed by five words. One of these has either the same meaning as the word in capitals, or the opposite meaning. Make two columns. Head the first S (for same *or* similar). Head the other O (for opposite). Then choose *one* word from each line and put it under S or O.

1. ADVANCE : prepare, retreat, succeed, conquer, lose.

2. RESPONSE : readiness, speech, answer, impose, explain.

3. COMPLEX : simple, complete, threefold, confused, excess.

4. TRANSPARENT : polished, eloquent, opaque, silver, shining.

5. DISTRIBUTE : arrange, decide, spread, collect, add.

6. FAITH : ignorance, knowledge, belief, opinion, judgment.

7. ESCORT : follow, precede, pursue, accompany, lead.

8. CONSPICUOUS : prominent, precious, spiky, respected, rich.

9. RESCUE : encounter, save, discover, accept, spend.

10. PERSEVERE : insist, resolve, excel, persist, score.

EXERCISE 3f

In each of the sentences below words have been underlined. Find a word in brackets that has the opposite meaning to these words. Write the word down.

1. I expect you will lift the package with great care.
   (carelessly, carefully, quickly, slowly, accurately)

2. John was told not to speak.
   (prohibited, obliged, forbidden, invited, hindered)

3. The visitors were allowed to come and go without any interference.
   (reluctantly, safely, dutifully, pleasantly, freely)

4. You speak as though you had a plum in your mouth.
   (badly, plainly, indistinctly, slowly, painfully)

5. Mary stuck to her job without thinking of giving in.
   (untiringly, persistently, hopelessly, thoughtlessly, happily)

1   2   3   4   5

If you turn the figures 2, 3, 4 and 5 round in your mind's eye until they are upright like No. 1, you will see that the second is facing in the opposite way to No. 1.

Which figure in each row below does not face in the same direction as No. 1, when it is placed upright?

1 | R₁   ⅃₂   R₃   Ʀ₄   Я₅
2 | N₁   Ƶ₂   И₃   Z₄   И₅
3 | J₁   ꓶ₂   ᒪ₃   ᒧ₄   ⌒₅
4 | S₁   ∾₂   ᔑ₃   ᔓ₄   ᔕ₅
5 | 4₁   ⅃₂   ⅄₃   ⅄₄   ⅃₅
6 | 6₁   ℮₂   b₃   ℴ₄   9₅
7 | ◣₁   ▷₂   ◸₃   ◿₄   ◹₅
8 | ⌐₁   ⌞₂   ⌐₃   ⌐₄   ⌐₅
9 | ◒₁   ◔₂   ◖₃   ◕₄   ◔₅
10 | ▯₁   ▱₂   ▱₃   ▱₄   ▱₅

4. PUTTING THINGS IN GROUPS

Example

Look at these words: Manchester, London, **Thames,** Liverpool, Birmingham. One is the odd one among the others. All are names of cities except for *Thames*, which is a river, so *Thames* is the odd one.

EXERCISE 4a

Look at each list of five things below and see if you can find the one that belongs to a different sort of group from the others. Write it down.

1. Elm, oak, tulip, ash, poplar.
2. Hat, coat, trousers, umbrella, scarf.
3. Red, blue, green, yellow, paper.
4. Swim, fly, run, sit, slide.
5. Sun, earth, candle, lamp, taper.
6. Chair, table, stool, bench, couch.
7. Ham, mutton, beef, lard, pork.
8. Road, avenue, street, square, lane.
9. Potato, apple, pear, plum, peach.
10. Car, train, engine, bus, tram.
11. Salmon, cod, crab, plaice, herring.
12. Horse, turkey, cow, pig, donkey.
13. Handkerchief, purse, bag, basket, pocket.
14. Soldier, sailor, airman, farmer, policeman.
15. Trumpet, violin, bugler, flute, guitar.
16. England, France, Paris, Germany, Spain.
17. Tea, brandy, coffee, milk, cocoa.
18. Peas, cabbage, beans, tomatoes, sprouts.
19. Kitten, puppy, cub, foal, ass.
20. 9, 7, 2, 5, 3.

EXERCISE 4b

What goes best with the three things named at the beginning of each line? Find the odd one and write it down giving it the same number as the number at the beginning of the line.

1. Miner, carpenter, bricklayer . . . doctor, lawyer, electrician, clergyman.
2. Canoe, yacht, liner . . . sailor, captain, steamer, sea.
3. II, III, IV . . . 2, 3, 4, IX.
4. Priest, vicar, bishop . . . church, padre, tower, cathedral.

5. House, bungalow, cottage . . . church, shop, flat, factory.

6. Silver, copper, gold . . . metal, copper, glass, marble.

7. River, brook, stream . . . pond, waterfall, sea, lake.

8. Congregation, crowd, audience . . . theatre, arena, stadium, assembly.

9. Family, tribe, nation . . . horde, clan, mob, club.

10. Cement, mortar, glue . . . lock, screw, solder, sand.

11. Clever, wise, thoughtful . . . stupid, clumsy, intelligent, dishonest.

12. Future, tomorrow, 1980 . . . yesterday, next year, last week, present.

13. Joy, happiness, pleasure . . . contentment, sorrow, misery, hatred.

14. Chase, follow, hunt . . . retreat, pursue, sweep, catch.

15. Graceful, beautiful, elegant . . . tall, short, handsome, ugly.

16. Work, business, labour . . . occupation, play, sleep, delight.

17. Science, mathematics, history . . . sums, geography, lessons, recreation.

18. Stop, prevent, hinder . . . desist, obstruct, upset, plan.

19. Waste, squander, dissipate . . . save, spill, hoard, spend.

20. Often, frequently, sometimes . . . always, repeatedly, seldom, perpetual.

EXERCISE 4c

In each line below one of the words is the name of the sort of thing of which the others are examples. Find this class name and write its number.

1. (1) Rose	(2) tulip	(3) flower	(4) daisy	(5) dandelion.
2. (1) King	(2) ruler	(3) president	(4) shah	(5) emperor.
3. (1) Wheat	(2) barley	(3) grain	(4) oats	(5) rye.
4. (1) Fuel	(2) coal	(3) logs	(4) peat	(5) coke.
5. (1) Hour	(2) week	(3) time	(4) day	(5) minute.
6. (1) Uncles	(2) aunts	(3) relations	(4) parents	(5) cousins.
7. (1) Cotton	(2) wool	(3) linen	(4) textiles	(5) silk.
8. (1) Cups	(2) plates	(3) saucers	(4) china	(5) dishes.
9. (1) Jewellery	(2) diamonds	(3) brooches	(4) bracelets	(5) necklaces.
10. (1) Pistols	(2) weapons	(3) guns	(4) spears	(5) swords.

5. SERIAL ORDER

Look at these numbers : 2, 4, 6, 8, 10. What number comes next? The answer is 12. Why? Because each number, after the first one, is 2 greater than the one before.

A set of numbers in some sort of order, like 2, 4, 6, 8, 10 or 1, 2, 3, 4, 5, or 10, 9, 8, 7, 6, is said to form a **series** or to be in **serial order.**

Here is another series : 100, 90, 80, 70, 60. What comes next? The answer is 50, because each number has to be 10 less than the one before. Let us try an easy series or two.

EXERCISE 5a

Write down the two numbers that should come next in each line.

1. 1, 3, 5, 7, 9, 11, ..., ...
2. 2, 5, 8, 11, 14, 17, ..., ...
3. 1, 2, 4, 7, 11, 16, ..., ...
4. 1, 4, 9, 16, 25, 36, ..., ...
5. 35, 28, 22, 17, 13, 10, ..., ...
6. 128, 64, 32, 16, 8, 4, ..., ...
7. 100, 92, 84, 78, 72, ..., ...
8. 7, 12, 17, 22, 27, 32, ..., ...
9. 9, 1, 8, 2, 7, 3, ..., ...
10. 1, 2, 3, 2, 3, 4, 3, 4, ..., ...

11. 729, 243, 81, 27, ..., ...
12. 30, 45, 60, 75, 90, ..., ...
13. 8, 4, 2, 1, ..., ...
14. 55, 11, 44, 22, 33, ..., ...
15. 203, 304, 405, 506, ..., ...
16. $\frac{7}{8}$, $\frac{6}{11}$, $\frac{5}{14}$, $\frac{4}{17}$, ..., ...
17. 4, 5, 5, 6, 6, 7, 7, 8, ..., ...
18. 1, 4, 8, 11, 15, 18, 22, ..., ...
19. 64, 16, 4, 1, ..., ...
20. 132, 243, 354, 465, ..., ...

EXERCISE 5b

Sometimes you may find that you are asked to pick out a number that should not have been put into the series. For example, 5 is out of place in the following series : 2, 4, 5, 6, 8, 10.
See if you can spot the wrong numbers in the following series. Write down the number which is out of place.

1. 1, 3, 5, 7, 9, 10, 11, 13, 15.
2. 1, 4, 9, 16, 20, 25, 36.
3. 91, 84, 77, 71, 63, 56, 49.
4. 8, 4, 2, 1, 0, $\frac{1}{2}$, $\frac{1}{4}$, $\frac{1}{8}$.
5. 1, 3, 6, 10, 14, 21, 28.

6. 2, 4, 8, 16, 30, 64, 128.
7. 12, 1, 11, 2, 10, 3, 8, 4.
8. $\frac{1}{2}$, $\frac{2}{3}$, $\frac{3}{4}$, $\frac{4}{5}$, $\frac{5}{8}$, $\frac{6}{7}$.
9. 100, 50, 10, 90, 50, 20, 80, 60, 30, 70.
10. 240, 176, 144, 126, 120.

EXERCISE 5c

Another way of setting the same kind of test is to ask you to fill in a missing number.

A number is missing from each line below. What is it?

1. 3, .., 9, 12, 15, 18, 21.
2. 2, 7, 12, 17, 22, .., 32.
3. 30, 27, 24, 21, .., 15, 12.
4. 1, 2, 2, 4, .., 6, 6, 8.
5. 17, .., 18, 15, 19, 14, 20, 13.
6. 45, 36, 28, .., 15, 10, 6.
7. 2, 1, 3, 2, 4, .., 5.
8. 4, 9, .., 25, 36, 49.
9. 103, 204, 305, ..., 507.
10. 18, 9, $4\frac{1}{2}$, .., $1\frac{1}{8}$, $\frac{9}{16}$.

EXERCISE 5d

Some examiners like to use letters instead of numbers in making a series. There should be nothing hard in these; they are usually easier than many of the series questions with numbers in them.

What two letters do you think should come next in each line below?

1. B, A, B, A, B, A, B.
2. C, A, D, A, E, A, F.
3. a, b, g, b, c, g, c, d.
4. z, a, y, b, x, c, w.
5. m, n, m, o, m, p, m.
6. x, y, k, w, x, l, v, w, m.
7. c, f, i, l, o, r.
8. a, c, f, j.
9. z, m, y, n, x, o, w, p.
10. a, a, b, c, b, b, c, d, c.

6. ANALOGIES

Let us think about things in pairs. A pair like **a cow and its calf** go together in the same way as **a mother and her child.** When two things can be seen to go together just as two other things go together we have what is called an **ANALOGY.**

The analogy we began with can be set out in this way :
Cow is to **calf** as **mother** is to **child.**

Here are some more analogies :

(1) **Four** is to **eight** as **eight** is to **sixteen** ; for just as **four** is half of **eight** so is **eight** half of **sixteen.**

(2) **Up** is to **down** as **before** is to **after** ; for **up** is the opposite of **down** just as **before** is the opposite of **after.**

Analogies are nearly always found in intelligence tests. Here are some easy examples.

EXERCISE 6a

What is the missing word at the end of each line ?

1. **Sugar** is to **sweet** as **sea-water** is to . . . .
2. **House** is to **man** as **nest** is to . . . .
3. **Melt** is to **butter** as **thaw** is to . . . .
4. **Speak** is to **shout** as **walk** is to . . . .
5. **Dead** is to **alive** as **day** is to . . . .
6. **Boot** is to **foot** as **glove** is to . . . .
7. **Men** are to **women** as **boys** are to . . . .
8. **Black** is to **white** as **good** is to . . . .
9. **Pen** is to **writer** as **screwdriver** is to . . . .
10. **Frame** is to **picture** as **cover** is to . . . .
11. **Dog** is to **sledge** as **horse** is to . . . .
12. **Light** is to **dark** as **quick** is to . . . .
13. **Ink** is to **pen** as **lead** is to . . . .
14. **Ship** is to **sea** as **aeroplane** is to . . . .
15. **Person** is to **crowd** as **tree** is to . . .

EXERCISE 6b

Finger is to **hand** as **toe** is to—**leg, foot, knee, ankle, instep** ?

The right answer is **foot,** because the toe is one of the five parts of the foot just as the finger is one of the five parts of the hand.

Pick out and write down the right answer in each example below.

1. **Tall** is to **short** as **broad** is to (**wide, narrow, long, straight, spacious**).
2. **Skating** is to **ice** as **swimming** is to (**racing, diving, water, snow, summer**).
3. **Sew** is to **needle** as **dig** is to (**garden, plant, spade, poke, perspire**).
4. **Happy** is to **laugh** as **sorry** is to (**smile, rejoice, cry, grumble, complain**).
5. **School** is to **pupils** as **army** is to (**teachers, generals, chiefs, soldiers, sailors**).
6. **Penny** is to **coin** as **hammer** is to (**money, tool, chisel, plane, saw**).
7. **Kind** is to **cruel** as **day** is to (**dusk, twilight, evening, morning, night**).
8. **Boot** is to **leather** as **sword** is to (**fight, kill, steel, battle, soldier**).
9. **Buying** is to **selling** as **earning** is to (**working, winning, purchasing, spending, losing**).
10. **Bird** is to **flying** as **snail** is to (**aeroplane, feathers, shell, creeping, hiding**).

EXERCISE 6c

There are other ways of putting analogy exercises before you. Instead of writing **sheep** is to **lamb** as **dog** is to **puppy,** you may read : **sheep : lamb : : dog : puppy** or **sheep : lamb . . . dog : puppy.**

Here is an exercise set out in that way.

Which word at the end of each line is needed to give the right answer ? Write it down.

1. Morning : evening . . . youth : (boy, girl, mid-day, twilight, age).
2. Merchant : selling . . . artist : (picture, painting, paints, brushes, oils).
3. Cow : milk . . . bee : (pollen, honey, flowers, sting, hive).
4. Mountain : hill . . . sea : (ocean, river, lake, water, wood).
5. Father : son . . . mother : (daughter, child, girl, sister, niece).
6. Food : man . . . petrol : (can, garage, motor car, stomach, driver).
7. Eating : solid . . . drinking : (tea, coffee, milk, cocoa, liquid).
8. Paper : wall . . . carpet : (rug, lino, floor, parquet, room).
9. Seat : sit . . . ladder : (rungs, wall, house, climb, fall).
10. Water : ship . . . air : (breathing, flying, aeroplane, airfield, tyre).

EXERCISE 6d

Perhaps the hardest task of all in doing an analogies exercise is to be given the first pair of connected words and then have to find another pair from a group of four or five words.

Example

Find two words in the brackets that are related to each other as the first pair are.

Father : mother . . . (uncle, son, brother, boy, aunt).

The answer is . . . uncle : aunt.

Find two words in the brackets that go together in the same way as the two words at the beginning of the line.

Write down each pair and give it the number at the beginning of the line.

1. Tailor : clothes . . . (furniture, hammer, carpenter, saw, wood).
2. Ice : water . . . (land, water, sky, steam, hills).
3. Soldier : rifle . . . (miner, sailor, lamp, tank, pickaxe).
4. Picture : see . . . (scenery, hear, travel, speech, dancing).
5. Kind : good . . . (honest, generous, well-mannered, well-dressed, polite).
6. Dream : sleep . . . (drown, swim, water, paddle, bathe).
7. Tom : Betty . . . (Bessie, Thomas, Lizzie, Tommy, Elizabeth).
8. Heavy : weight . . . (long, short, distant, length, breadth).
9. Fear : tremble . . . (comic, laugh, pleasure, sorrow, funny).
10. Country : nation . . . (clan, family, mother, house, home).

EXERCISE 6e

Find and write down the word needed to complete the analogy. It is one of the five at the end of each example.

1. AB : CD . . . FG : (AC/HI/BD/IJ/JK).
2. This : that . . . here : (where/whence/thither/there/whither).
3. 4 : 9 . . . 16 : (20/24/64/81/100).
4. He : man . . . she : (girl/aunt/mother/woman/queen).
5. One : many . . . star : (planet/sun/constellation/universe/sky).
6. Child : girl . . . parent : (child/mother/grandfather/uncle/aunt).

7. Departure : arrival . . . go : (leave/stop/terminus/platform/come).
8. Chop : steak . . . mutton : (ham/pork/beef/veal/cutlet).
9. Hour : time . . . mile : (furlong/day/distance/speed/race).
10. Soon : never . . . near : (ever/nowhere/somewhere/distant/far off).

EXERCISE 6f

Analogies may also be expressed in this way.

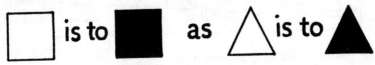

See if you can work an exercise of this kind.

Which figure goes with No. 3 in the same way as No. 2 goes with No. 1 ?

Write down 4, 5, 6 or 7 to show the correct answer.

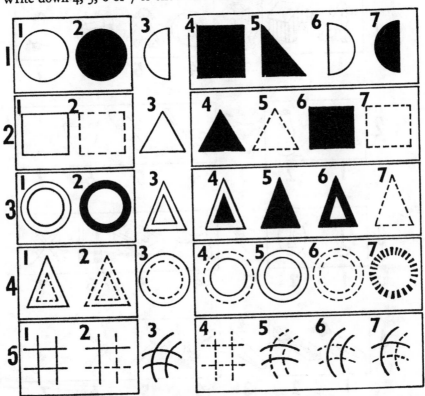

EXERCISE 6g

Look at the pictures below.

No. 1 is to No. 2 as No. 3 is to one of the remaining four. Which one of the four is it? The answer is No. 5, because just as a *foot* is to a *shoe*, so is a *hand* to a *glove*. *Glove* is, therefore, the answer.

Now work the following exercise :

Find one of the four pictures that bears the same relation to No. 3 as No. 2 does to No. 1. In other words, No. 1 is to No. 2 as No. 3 is to one of the remainder. Which is it : 4, 5, 6 or 7?

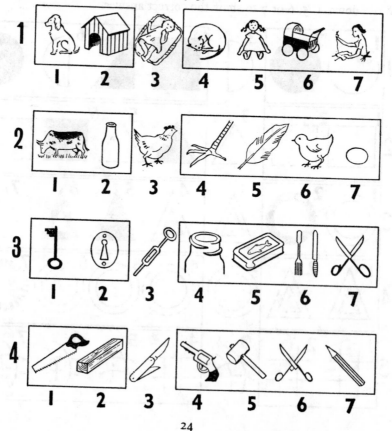

7. ARRANGING THINGS IN ORDER

Other things besides numbers and letters can be arranged in order. Animals, for example, can be arranged in order of SIZE ; girls and boys can be arranged in order of AGE ; policemen can be arranged in order of HEIGHT ; weights can be arranged in order of HEAVINESS ; kings and queens can be arranged in order of the TIMES they lived in ; and so on.

Let us begin with some animals, birds, fishes and insects which can be arranged in the order of their size.

EXERCISE 7a

Which creature is the largest in size in each line ? When you have picked it out, write its name down.

1. Dog, ant, horse, bee, pony.
2. Sprat, codfish, herring, shark, plaice.
3. Robin, wren, thrush, crow, eagle.
4. Kitten, hare, rabbit, mouse, rat.
5. Butterfly, wasp, bat, dog, horse.
6. Crab, oyster, turtle, winkle, lobster.
7. Lion, tiger, elephant, leopard, bear.
8. Mole, weasel, ferret, badger, squirrel.
9. Cow, sheep, pig, calf, lamb.
10. Hen, duck, turkey, goose, pheasant.

EXERCISE 7b

Pick out the smallest thing in size in each line and write down its name.

1. Football, orange, tennis-ball, marble, golf-ball.
2. Daisy, rose, sunflower, tulip, daffodil.
3. Apple, pear, lemon, grapefruit, plum.
4. 5p, 2p, 10p, $\frac{1}{2}$p, 1p.
5. Church, palace, cottage, mansion, cathedral.
6. Violin, piano, flute, bugle, bagpipes.
7. Nose, eye, ear, chin, forehead.
8. Cannon, tank, torpedo, bullet, shell.
9. Sun, earth, moon, meteor, Mars.
10. Tree, trunk, twig, branch, leaf.

EXERCISE 7c

Re-arrange in order in your mind the five things in each line below. When you have done so, write down the name of the middle one.

1. Father, boy, youth, grandfather, infant.   2. House, town, street, county, country.
3. Lake, sea, ocean, puddle, pond.   4. Foot, head, knee, chest, neck.
5. Minute, hour, second, day, week.   6. Chapter, page, letter, word, book.
7. Shirt, overcoat, jacket, vest, waistcoat.   8. Kennel, nest, house, castle, mansion.
9. Australia, China, Great Britain, Monaco, France.
10. Canoe, battleship, yacht, liner, rowing-boat.

EXERCISE 7d

You will find below some sets of words that are used in describing things. Arrange them in order and write down the name of the middle one.

1. Huge, enormous, minute, small, large.
2. Never, sometimes, generally, seldom, always.
3. Evil, naughty, wicked, good, virtuous.
4. Interested, keen, apathetic, indifferent, enthusiastic.
5. Fond, harsh, loving, hateful, friendly.
6. Black, white, dark, grey, light.
7. Cold, boiling, hot, tepid, warm.
8. Some, all, none, most, few.
9. Better, worse, bad, good, best.
10. Quick, slow, swift, leisurely, lightning-like.

EXERCISE 7e

You will find four things named in each line below. They are followed by the names of four other things, one of which can be fitted in to a place among the first four. Pick it out and write down both its name and the order in which it should come.

Example

Basement, ground floor, first floor, attic . . . cellar, second floor, storeroom, kitchen.

Answer : Second floor (4).

1. Semi-quaver, quaver, crotchet, semi-breve . . . rest, breve, bar, minim.
2. Stroke, pat, smack, clout . . . crush, slap, blow, thrust.

3. Creep, walk, march, run . . . stroll, rise, relax, scuttle.
4. March, May, July, September . . . February, November, December, October.
5. Silent, quiet, sounding, loud . . . full, deafening, hoarse, inaudible.
6. Solo, duet, quartet, quintet . . . sonata, sextet, trio, symphony.
7. Pink, rose-red, vermilion, crimson . . . scarlet, buff, orange, green.
8. North, north-east, east, south . . . west, south-west, south-east, north-west.
9. Rare, infrequent, frequent, constant . . . daily, perpetual, often, common.
10. Wallet, attaché-case, suit-case, trunk . . . despatch-case, canister, crate, haversack.

EXERCISE 7f

Think of the order in which you would place the following and then write the number of the one that comes in the middle.

8. MIXED SENTENCES

Sometimes an intelligence test contains nonsense sentences that can be made quite sensible by changing the order of the words. This you are asked to do and show how you have done it. Try the first exercise below and you will see what is meant.

EXERCISE 8a

Two words in each sentence below ought to change places to make sense. Write the sentences out as they should be.

1. Carrots eat donkeys.
2. Milk sometimes swallows Mary.
3. Every day the east rises in the sun.
4. My room is in a bed upstairs.
5. Say did you what about John ?
6. How hat you get that did ?
7. Come Maud the garden into.
8. Where all you been have this time ?
9. Kettle makes tea with water which she boils in a mother.
10. Ice is than colder water.

EXERCISE 8b

Put each of the following into a sensible order and say whether it is true or false.

1. Sunday week is the day of the last.
2. Fine in the sky is blue weather.
3. Great babies take usually care of their mothers.
4. Years days leap contain 365.
5. Rule as bread is a than cheaper cake.
6. Lilies kind roses of are a know you.
7. The snow with often the wind comes south.
8. Begin in the meadows spring to flowers in appear.
9. Make one twenty-five day hours.
10. Largest hemisphere in Australia is the island the English.

28

EXERCISE 8c

Put the words below into the right order and write down the word needed to make sense.

1. Weather in time is winter the . . .
2. The doctor when I to feel go I . . .
3. They grow when girls become up . . .
4. The every east rises in the sun . . .
5. In the first month is January the . . .
6. Easily with mix does oil not . . .
7. Into it boils when water turns . . .
8. Longest the days are in the nights and are June . . .
9. Before a pencil must a pen or you have you can . . .
10. Played without a person cannot be a piano by . . .

EXERCISE 8d

Re-arrange the words in the following sentences to make sense and then write down the **last word only** in each sentence.

1. Early summer in buttercups appear.
2. Enough lighting for it is dark up.
3. Foggy persons like few days.
4. The look wall on at the shadow.
5. Of ice cream are fond children.
6. Socks up his told was to pull he.
7. Of London is the England capital.
8. Trusted people can honest be.
9. Good warmth is because it gives us fire.
10. Like another he will John where friend find ?

EXERCISE 8e

Re-arrange the words in the following sentences so that they will make sense **if one more word** can be added. Find this word among those in the brackets and write it down.

1. Sea deep in the water is the (fish, salt, sailor, bones).
2. The colder pole at the north it is near than (equator, moon, milky way, tomorrow).
3. The morning was for late boy (early, today, school, prize).
4. The bayonets crossed to make their soldiers a (battle, barrier, noise, uproar).
5. The netball of Mary is the school captain (goal, champion, team, spectator).
6. The time just up to a lorry pulled avoid in (midnight, wheels, collision, brakes, driving).
7. I have been flat without looking for a (daily, knowing, carefulness, success).
8. His expensive mother he bought an (father, past, present, future).
9. The White visitors at his President entertained the (House, party, games, chess).
10. We parents that were sure had been our (nowhere, children, lost, dead).

29

9. BEST REASONS

Find the right reason for each of the questions asked or statements made below. Answer the questions by writing (a), (b), (c) or (d). The first two are done for you.

Why do we use soap in washing ?
    (a) It smells nice.
    (b) It makes a good lather.
    (c) It removes dirt quickly.
    (d) It softens the water.
The answer is (c).

Why should we keep the windows a little open in a room ?
    (a) To change the air in the room.
    (b) To prevent the windows from getting stuck.
    (c) To let any warm air escape.
    (d) To be able to know what is happening outside.
The answer is (a).

1. **Why do we place flowers on the table ?**
    (a) To keep the air pure.
    (b) To make the table look pleasing.
    (c) To take away the smell of bad food.
    (d) To cover up any dirty marks on the tablecloth.

2. **Policemen are needed.**
Because (a) We like to see them in uniform.
    (b) People do wrong if not watched.
    (c) We have to find jobs for everyone.
    (d) We want to see that the laws are obeyed.

3. **We send children to school.**
Because (a) They are best taught there.
    (b) Parents want them out of their way.
    (c) They would be a nuisance in the streets.
    (d) They can meet their friends there.

4. **Eggs are cheapest in the spring.**
Because (a) They are smallest in size in the spring.
    (b) We need more eggs in the spring.
    (c) More eggs are laid in the spring.
    (d) They are harder to sell in the spring.

5. **Why are children taught to be honest ?**

    (a) To keep them from stealing from us.
    (b) To earn rewards for pleasing us.
    (c) To get on in life.
    (d) To enjoy a clear conscience.

6. **Sailors do not drink sea-water.**

    Because (a) It is never clean.
    (b) It has an unpleasant taste.
    (c) It increases their thirst instead of relieving it.
    (d) It makes them lazy and sleepy.

7. **White clouds float in the sky.**

    Because (a) They are lighter than the air below them.
    (b) They can move about easily there.
    (c) They look much better there.
    (d) We like to see them there.

8. **Why does snow stay on the mountain tops in summer ?**

    (a) It is nearer the sun there.
    (b) It is too cold there for it to melt.
    (c) Nothing else will stay there.
    (d) No one has ever disturbed it there.

9. **We keep animals in a zoo.**

    Because (a) They are best out of the way there.
    (b) They like being there.
    (c) They can only be seen and studied by us there.
    (d) They would not be properly looked after anywhere else.

10. **Why do children do composition exercises in school ?**

    (a) To keep them occupied when teacher is busy.
    (b) To help them to learn to write what they think and feel.
    (c) To learn good handwriting.
    (d) To learn their grammar.

11. **Why do bacon and eggs make a good breakfast ?**

    (a) They are so expensive.
    (b) They have such a lovely taste.
    (c) They contain all the right food elements.
    (d) They are easily cooked.

12. **Why are shoes usually made of leather ?**

    (a) Leather is plentiful.
    (b) Leather takes a good polish.
    (c) Leather wears well and keeps out the wet.
    (d) Leather is cheap.

10. REASONING–SIMPLE INFERENCES

When you draw a conclusion from something you already know, you are making an inference. When you draw the right conclusions or make the right inferences, you are reasoning well.

Try this :

1. You know that Jack sits on the right of John and that John sits on the right of Joe. Who sits in the middle ?

The answer is John. The inference is correct.

EXERCISE 10a

Find the right answer in the brackets after each question and write it down.

1. John is taller than David but shorter than Mark. Who is the tallest? (John, David, Mark.)

2. Peter has more marbles than Paul but not so many as Percy. Who has least of all? (Peter, Paul, Percy.)

3. In the spring crocuses come up before tulips but after snowdrops. Which come up first ? (Crocuses, tulips, snowdrops.)

4. Tom did not get so many sums right as Terry but he got more right than Tim. Who got the least number right ? (Tom, Terry, Tim.)

5. Mary can jump nine centimetres farther than Molly. Margaret can jump two centimetres farther than Molly. Molly can jump five centimetres farther than Miriam and Miriam four centimetres farther than Maizie. Who would be placed midway in jumping order ? (Mary, Molly, Margaret, Miriam, Maizie.)

6. Joe was late for school. Ten minutes later he was followed by Jack. John arrived five minutes before Jack. Who arrived last ? (Joe, Jack, John.)

7. A box full of chocolates weighs 1 kg. The box when empty weighs 150 g. How much do the chocolates in the box weigh ? (700 g, 800 g, 850 g, 750 g, 900 g.)

8. I want to find a certain number which I will call X. It is four times as great as another number which is two less than twenty. What is X ? (24, 36, 48, 72, 96.)

9. A man bought a TV set two days before his birthday. Three days after his birthday it broke down. It broke down on January 2nd, 1970. When did he buy it ? (December 28th, 1969 ; December 29th, 1969 ; December 30th, 1969 ; December 31st, 1969 ; January 1st, 1970.)

10. If the smallest of the following fruits were the most costly, which of them should I have to pay most for ? (Orange, plum, grapefruit, grape, lemon.)

11. Jack is twice as old as he was five years ago. His mother was then six times as old as he was. She is now 35 years old.
   (a) How old is Jack ?
   (b) How old was his mother when Jack was five ?
   (c) How old will Jack be when his mother is 50 ?
   (d) How old was Jack's mother when he was born ?
   (e) What is the difference between Jack's age and his mother's ?

12. Read the following letter :
   24, High Street, London.   Sunday, April 28th.
       Dear John, You left your mac here last Friday. Perhaps you will call for it when you pass this way on Wednesday next. I shall be going away on Friday next. Yours sincerely, Peter.
   (a) What was the date when the mac was left behind ? (April 22nd, 23rd, 24th, 25th, 26th, 27th.)
   (b) Give the date when John was expected to call for his mac. (April 28th, 29th, 30th, May 1st, 2nd, 3rd, 4th.)
   (c) On what date will Peter be going away ? (May 1st, 2nd, 3rd, 4th, 5th, 6th.)
   (d) In the year when the note was written, on which day of the week did May begin ?
   (e) For how many days did Peter expect the mac to remain at his house ?

13. Look at the following table. It shows how many articles were sold by a jeweller during a week.

	Watches	Rings	Brooches
Monday	2	3	2
Tuesday	4	7	5
Wednesday	7	2	3
Thursday	5	8	6
Friday	7	9	8
Saturday	8	10	7

Now answer the questions below :
   (a) How many articles were sold in the week ?
   (b) On which day were most articles sold ?
   (c) How many rings and brooches were sold on Friday and Saturday ?
   (d) Which were sold most of in the week : rings, brooches or watches ?
   (e) When were fewest articles sold ?

A 3   33

14. Here is another table that shows you which children in a group of five like the fruits named. For instance, John likes every one except pineapples.

	Apples	Oranges	Bananas	Pineapples	Grapes
John	✓	✓	✓		✓
Mary	✓		✓	✓	
Peter		✓		✓	✓
Ann	✓		✓	✓	✓
David	✓	✓			✓

Write the correct answers to the questions below :

(a) Who likes pineapples but not bananas ?

(b) Who likes apples and oranges but not bananas ?

(c) Who likes oranges and grapes but not pineapples ?

(d) Who likes apples, pineapples and grapes ?

(e) Who likes oranges but not apples ?

15. Read what you are told about the following four boys, Tim, Tom, Terry and Ted, and then answer the questions below.

Tim and Terry are tall.

Terry and Tom are dark.

Tim and Ted are handsome.

Write the correct answers to these questions :

(a) Who is both tall and handsome ?

(b) Who is neither tall nor handsome ?

(c) Who is both tall and dark ?

(d) Who is tall but not handsome ?

(e) Who is handsome but not dark ?

34

11. LOGICAL DEDUCTIONS

or " Putting Two and Two Together "

Suppose you know the following four facts :

(a) London lies to the south of Birmingham ;
(b) Liverpool lies to the north of Bristol ;
(c) Bristol lies to the south of Birmingham ;
(d) Birmingham lies to the south of Liverpool.

Which two of these four facts help you to say that **Liverpool lies to the north of London ?**   The answer is (a) and (d).   In getting your answer you have made a logical deduction.   In other words you have reasoned correctly from what you already know and come to a logical conclusion. In the test that follows you will have to choose two sentences that make the sentence in bold letters a true statement.

EXERCISE 11a

Find two sentences that make the fifth one true. Answer the questions by writing (a), (b), (c) or (d).
    The first is done for you.

(a) Ayville is north of Beeville.
(b) Seaville is west of Beeville.
(c) Deeville is south of Beeville.
(d) Deeville is south-west of Seaville.
    Ayville is north of Deeville.
    The answer is (a) and (c).

1. (a) John was born two years after Jack.
   (b) Jack is younger than Peter.
   (c) Tom was born before Jack.
   (d) Peter is not so old as Tom.
   Tom is older than John.

2. (a) Sam and Fred are tall.
   (b) Fred and Frank are fair.
   (c) Frank and Eric are short.
   (d) Eric and Sam are dark.
   Sam is tall and dark.

3. (a) Mary and Jane speak French.
   (b) Jane and Doris speak German.
   (c) Doris and Susan speak Italian.
   (d) Susan and Mary speak Dutch.
   Jane speaks French but not Italian.

4. (a) Silver is heavier than copper.
   (b) Gold is heavier than lead.
   (c) Iron is lighter than copper.
   (d) Lead is heavier than silver.
   Gold is heavier than silver.

5. (a) Forty boys passed the entrance examination.
   (b) Thirty boys answered more than half the questions.
   (c) Twenty boys answered less than half the questions.
   (d) Ten boys failed in the entrance examination.
   Fifty boys sat for the entrance examination.

6. (a) Only citizens over 18 have a vote.
   (b) Marjorie is a citizen aged 25.
   (c) Arthur will be a 20-year-old citizen next year.
   (d) Citizen John was born last year.
   Arthur has the right to a vote.

7. (a) More than half the boys at school play cricket.
   (b) More than half the boys at school play tennis.
   (c) Some boys at school play cricket and badminton.
   (d) Some boys at school play badminton and tennis.
   Some boys at school play tennis and cricket.

8. (a) All the boys in Form Three won attendance certificates.
   (b) All who won attendance certificates were given a book.
   (c) Some who were given a book were also given a pencil case.
   (d) All who were given a pencil case were in the school choir.
   Some who were in the school choir were given a book.

9. (a) Mary is on the tennis court.
   (b) All the girls play tennis in the summer time.
   (c) One of the girls in the tennis team is Mary.
   (d) All the girls on the tennis court are actually playing tennis.
   Mary is playing tennis.

10. (a) Henry and Hector like swimming.
    (b) Henry and Harold like cricket.
    (c) Harold and Horace dislike football.
    (d) Horace and Hector like skating.
    Hector likes swimming and skating.

EXERCISE 11b

Here are some riddles for you to reason out. They will catch you if you are not careful, so be sure of taking the right steps to get your answer.

1. I have four legs but I cannot walk on them. I have a back but I cannot bend it. When you want me to move I cannot do it myself. And yet people find me of great use. What am I?
   (a) A boy; (b) A donkey; (c) A table; (d) A chair; (e) A tortoise.
   Which is the right answer: (a), (b), (c), (d) or (e)?

2. I work only by night. Many people are glad to see me working. I like to help others working at night to find their way about. I don't work myself, however, unless I am made to do so. What am I?
   (a) A burglar; (b) A policeman; (c) A lighthouse; (d) A dynamo; (e) A detective.
   Which is the right answer: (a), (b), (c), (d) or (e)?

3. I play a lot but I sit down to it.   I make plenty of noise at times but people seem to like it.   Yet you would not want me to play as I do in a small room.   What am I ?
(a) A monkey ; (b) A brass band ; (c) A chess player ; (d) A footballer ; (e) A darts player.
Which is the right answer : (a), (b), (c), (d) or (e) ?

4. We have tongues but we cannot speak.   Most people look down on us when we are in the street and yet they find us useful.   This is because they rely on us to keep them dry and warm.   What are we ?
(a) Shoes ; (b) Servants ; (c) Newspaper sellers ; (d) Beggars ; (e) Umbrellas.
Which is the right answer : (a), (b), (c), (d) or (e) ?

5. I can touch you but you will never see me.   When all is still and quiet I am never about.   But everyone knows when I am on the move.   Then I feel strong.   Then you know I am coming.   What am I ?
(a) An earthquake ; (b) A giant ; (c) A lion ; (d) An elephant ; (e) The wind.
Which is the right answer : (a), (b), (c), (d) or (e) ?

6. I am not alive though I can nod and smile.   I like to do what you do but often it seems to be just the opposite.   When you turn your back on me I disappear from your sight.   What am I ?
(a) A tailor's dummy ; (b) Your twin brother (or sister) ; (c) Your image in the looking glass ; (d) Your teacher ; (e) Your photograph.
Which is the right answer : (a), (b), (c), (d) or (e) ?

7. We have no mouths or hands.   Yet we are alive.   Some people place us on the table.   What are we ?
(a) Flowers ; (b) Goldfish ; (c) Mince-pies ; (d) Knives and Forks.
Which is the right answer : (a), (b), (c) or (d) ?

8. You cannot do without me.   And yet I run away whenever I get the chance.   I am found in the sky, in the ground and out at sea.   What am I ?
(a) Clouds ; (b) Water ; (c) Ships ; (d) Seagulls.
Which is the right answer : (a), (b), (c) or (d) ?

9. Everyone needs me.   I come to them very quietly.   I usually come at night but I like to visit little babies in the daytime as well.   What am I ?
(a) The Postman ; (b) Sleep ; (c) Father Christmas ; (d) Good Luck.
Which is the right answer : (a), (b), (c) or (d) ?

10. I have a ring but no one has ever seen it.   I have a tongue but I cannot speak by myself.   But if you hit me I usually make a loud noise.   What am I ?
(a) A drum ; (b) A bunch of keys ; (c) A bell ; (d) A rattle.
Which is the right answer : (a), (b), (c) or (d) ?

11. I can be heard but I am never seen.   I come out of people's mouths but I never go in.   When you hear me you usually know whose mouth I have come from.   What am I ?
(a) A Breath ; (b) Words ; (c) A Voice ; (d) Teeth.
Which is the right answer : (a), (b), (c) or (d) ?

12. CODES

A code consists of signs or symbols that have a secret meaning. A shop-keeper, for example, may wish to mark the prices of the various articles, which he sells, on the articles themselves, but for his own purposes only. One way of marking them would be to use letters instead of figures—for example, putting A for 1, B for 2, C for 3, and so on. Using the code he would write C·FA for £3·61 and A·BD for £1·24.

In the kind of intelligence test which you are most likely to meet, code questions are put in the following way.

EXERCISE 12a

In a code, numbers are replaced by letters. A stands for 9, B for 8, C for 7 and D for 6. Find the right answers to the following questions.

1. What letter would you write for nought (0) ? G H I J K L.
2. What letter would you write for 2 ? F G H I J K.
3. What letter would you write for 4 ? C D E F G H.
4. How many letters are needed in the above code ? 12, 11, 10, 9, 8, 7.
5. What does FI·JD stand for ? £410·60, £0·41, £41·06, £14·60, £4·10.
6. What does IJ·DJ stand for ? £1·60, £106·00, £0·10, £16·00, £10·60.
7. How would £5·60 be written ? ED·J, E·DI, E·JI, E·DJ, E·JD.
8. How would £150·00 be written ? IEJ·II, IJE·II, IEJ·JJ, EJI·EE, JIE·JJ.
9. How would £28·75 be written ? HB·CE, BH·CE, HB·CD, IB·CE, HI·CE.
10. Write down the meaning of the following message in this code.

2165/6596/72154.

EXERCISE 12b

A B C D E F G H I J K L M N O P Q R S T U V W X Y Z

In this exercise you will have to find out the code for yourself. It may be different for each question. You may be told, for example, that DPNF means COME, and you will ask : What is the code ? The answer is that it consists of letters that are in every case those that stand just before them in the alphabet. D for C, P for O, N for M, F for E :

D   P   N   F
C   O   M   E

Now try the questions that follow.
Which are the right answers ?

38

1. If CBE means BAD, then GMBH means   (good, food, flag, flog, glad).
2. If GTQQX means HURRY, then RSNO means   (soon, stop, ship, shop, step).
3. If RGCEG means PEACE, then YCT means   (war, was, wet, web, wax).
4. If NQXG means LOVE, then ECMG means   (good, calm, cake, gale, calf).
5. If NCL means PEN, then GLI means   (elk, ilk, ink, egg, its).

A	B	C	D	E	F	G	H	I	J	K	L	M
Z	Y	X	W	V	U	T	S	R	Q	P	O	N

6. If XZG means CAT, then DOG should be written as (gad, owt, wlt, xog, taw).
7. If YVZI means BEAR, then DLOU means (lion, wolf, deer, pony, lynx).
8. If XSZRI means CHAIR, then TABLE should be written as (gzyov, vgzyo, gayoe, gayov).
9. If SLFHG means HOUSE, then HGIVVG means (garden, avenue, street, stairs, window).
10. If LOOK is written as OLLP, then SEE should be written as (vhh, hvh, hhv, vhv, hvv).

EXERCISE 12c

A	B	C	D	E	F	G	H	I	J	K	L	M
Z	Y	X	W	V	U	T	S	R	Q	P	O	N

In a secret way of writing (in the above code) COME AT ONCE, FATHER VERY ILL is written as XLNV ZG LMXV, UZGSVI EVIB ROO.

Choose, from among the four ways given, the correct way of writing the following words :

1. UNCLE . . . . FNXLV, EMXOV, EMCOV, FMXOV.
2. AUNTIE . . . . ZENGRV, ZEMGIV, ZFMGRV, ZENGIV.
3. COUSIN . . . . XOFHRM, XLFSRM, XLUHRM, XLFHRM.
4. MOTHER . . . . NOGSVI, NOTSVI, NLGSVI, NLGSEI.
5. FIT AND WELL . . . . URG ZMV DEOO, URG ZNV DEOO, URG ZMW DVOO, URG ZNV DVOO.

X	Y	Z	A	B	C	D	E	F	G	H	I	J	L
Z	Y	X	W	V	U	T	S	R	Q	P	O	N	M

Using the above code, find the right way of writing the following words.

6. JOY . . . . nix, oiy, miy, niy.
7. FEAR. . . . . rswf, rtzf, swfr, brsf.
8. HOPE . . . . plhs, pihs, phiz, hips.
9. GRIEF . . . . qfisr, qfofr, qfisf, qfosr.
10. SORROW . . . . . . eiffiz, eoffoa, eiffia, eaffio.

39

In a secret way of writing

COME AT ONCE QUICKLY—VERA is written as

GSQI EX SRGI UYMGOPC—ZIVE.

1. Which month of the year would be written in this code as RSZIQFIV ?
2. Using the same code, what would you put down for this ?   MEET ME ANY TIME.
3. A message in the same secret writing is set out below.   What does it mean ?   You will have to guess *one* letter.   GERX CSY FI UYMIX ?

   The word MISTAKENLY is used as a code word by a shopkeeper so that
   M = 1, I = 2, S = 3, and so on.
4. What is the price of an article marked S·KL ?
5. What is the price of an article marked AN·TI ?
6. How would you write £5·15 in this code ?
7. How would you write £47·95 in this code ?
8. In a certain secret code

   MUST SURRENDER IF NO HELP ARRIVES TODAY is written as
   SAYZ YAXXKTJKX OL TU NKRV GXXOBKY ZUJGE

   In the same code how would you write the following message ?
   TRY TO FIND MARY FOR US.
9. Which day of the week is named in this code as ZAKYJGE ?
10. Write down the words APRIL AND MAY in this code.

13. COMPLETION TESTS

In a completion test you are asked to finish a sentence or phrase by filling in the words that have been omitted (or left out). You may, for example, be asked to find a word to complete the sentences. You will not need to be told what it is

The . . . rises in the east.

or The sun . . . in the east.

or The sun rises in the . . .

You will now be ready to begin the first exercise in " completion."

EXERCISE 13a

Find and write down the words in the brackets that will best complete the following sentences.

1. Grass is . . . . (Blue, yellow, red, green, grey.)
2. A dozen is eight . . . than a score. (Over, times, less, also, more.)
3. To smooth a plank of wood a . . . is required. (Hammer, chisel, screwdriver, saw, plane.)
4. Before entering someone else's room you should . . . on the door. (Bang, kick, knock, slam, press.)
5. When you write with a pencil you can not make . . . . (Mistakes, figures, blots, letters, alterations.)
6. The . . . days of the year are in the summer. (Shortest, coldest, happiest, longest, coolest.)
7. Metal bars . . . when they are heated. (Fall, snap, expand, ring, explode.)
8. In very cold weather water taps often . . . . (Run, sag, thaw, freeze, drip.)
9. When snow is . . . it is usually powdery. (Dry, wet, warm, moist, frozen.)
10. I could not get your collar stiffer. I had no . . . . (Soap, starch, powder, soda.)

EXERCISE 13b

This is a harder exercise because you have to find two words instead of one in order to complete each sentence.

Find out and write down two words in each sentence below to make good sense.

1. Roses are sometimes . . . (thorny, red, large, pretty) but buttercups are usually . . . (early, late, big, yellow).
2. The lion is a . . . animal (zoo, fearless, large, brown) but rabbits are quite . . . (clever, strong, deaf, timid).
3. I feel . . . (guilty, satisfied, strange, hungry) although I have just had a good . . . (trial, run, meal, drink).

4. If you . . . (eat, sleep, drink, work) hard, you will soon . . . (exceed, waken, finish, decide).
5. Lace up your . . . (curtains, handkerchief, shoes, gloves) and make a tidy . . . (hole, knot, face, aspect).
6. This letter requires a . . . (pen, pencil, stamp, envelope) before you . . . it (open, write, post, receive).
7. Whatever you . . . (say, think, send, publish), keep it to . . . (Christmas, myself, others, yourself).
8. Whenever you see . . . (stars, fairies, lightning, wonders), you can expect . . . (rain, thunder, holidays, prizes).
9. Just as you cannot make . . . without flour (wheat, ovens, bread, corn), so you cannot . . . castles without stones (build, plan, capture, move).
10. You may leave . . . (alone, early, home, the rest) provided that you . . . your work (like, begin, finish, hate).

EXERCISE 13c

Find and write down the word in brackets that is required to complete the following story.

1. A visitor who was staying in a . . . city (noisy, dirty, strange, familiar)
2. lost his . . . (mother, money, way, wallet).
3. What could he . . . ? (realise, do, feel, write)
4. Fortunately, he saw a . . . (lamp, policeman, bus, shop).
5. He went up to . . . and said (him, it, see, them).
6. " I am . . . at City House (shopping, cleaning, staying, working).
7. Will you please tell me . . . to get there ? " (when, how, where, what)
8. " . . . I will," was the reply. (perhaps, somehow, certainly, bother)
9. " Take the . . . turning on the left (right, wrong, busy, first),
10. and you will see it . . . you." (behind, approach, surprise, before)

EXERCISE 13d

In this " story " you require a certain amount of knowledge if you are to work it correctly but it is everyday knowledge.

Choose and write down the words in brackets that make the best sense.

1. From . . . we not only (iron, gold, coal, slate)
2. get gas but many valuable . . . (metals, substances, insects, plants).
3. Some of these make our . . . fertile (factories, fields, homes, shops).
4. Some provide us with . . . when we are ill (medicines, doctors, nurses, X-rays).
5. Some enable us to make . . . cabinets (box, house, radio, horse).
6. Some are used to . . . wounds (make, heal, inflict, renew).
7. Some give us . . . for the roads (stones, blocks, kerbs, tar).
8. Some provide . . . for motor-cars (brakes, lamps, wheels, petrol).
9. Some give us . . . for sugar (powder, substitutes, cakes, fruit)
10. and some are used in making . . . (explosives, engines, walls, furniture).

14. DEFINITIONS AND PROPERTIES

(a) Definitions.

What is a **screwdriver** ? It may be hard to say exactly but it is easy to find the phrase that best describes it when four are given you to choose from. Would it be :

1. Something made of wood and metal
2. A tool used by a carpenter
3. Something that drives a screw *or*
4. An instrument for putting nails into wood ?

The answer, of course, is No. 2.

EXERCISE 14a

Here are some easy questions for you to work. Write (*1*), (*2*), (*3*) or (*4*) for your answer.

1. Which answer tells you best what a **saucepan** is ?
   (*1*) A household article
   (*2*) A domestic necessity
   (*3*) A cooking utensil
   (*4*) A kitchen aid.
2. Which of the following tells you best what a **leg** is ?
   (*1*) It is fitted into shoes
   (*2*) It is for walking on
   (*3*) It is for standing on
   (*4*) It is one of the lower parts of your body below the trunk.
3. Which sentence tells you best what a **puppy** is ?
   (*1*) It is a playful creature
   (*2*) It is a baby dog
   (*3*) It has a tail that wags
   (*4*) It is just the opposite of a kitten.
4. Which of the following tells you best what a **house** is ?
   (*1*) A living space
   (*2*) A building
   (*3*) A store structure
   (*4*) A building made for living in.
5. Which of the following tells us best what a **whale** is ?
   (*1*) The largest fish
   (*2*) The largest of all sea animals
   (*3*) A warmblooded denizen of the deep
   (*4*) A sea monster.
6. Which of the following tells you best what a **sword** is ?
   (*1*) A weapon used by a soldier in fighting
   (*2*) A weapon of war
   (*3*) A sharp-bladed instrument
   (*4*) A pointed knife-like thing.
7. Which of the following tells you best what a **nut** is ?
   (*1*) An enclosed fruit
   (*2*) The seed of certain trees
   (*3*) A shell-like fruit
   (*4*) The hard-shelled fruit of some trees.

8. Which of the following tells you best what an **umbrella** is ?
    (*1*) A shelter from rain
    (*2*) An article that can be held over the head as a shelter from rain
    (*3*) Something that can be spread out to keep off the rain
    (*4*) A shade from rain and sun.

9. Which of the following tells you best what a **plum** is ?
    (*1*) A small fruit
    (*2*) A fruit used in making jam
    (*3*) A soft sweet fruit
    (*4*) A fleshy fruit with a stone in the centre.

10. Which of the following tells you best what a **chair** is ?
    (*1*) An object made of wood
    (*2*) A piece of furniture
    (*3*) A piece of furniture made for sitting on
    (*4*) An article used in the dining-room.

(*b*) **Properties,** or what things always have.
    What has every **room** ?   Is it : (*1*) a table (*2*) chairs (*3*) pictures (*4*) space ?
    The answer is (*4*).

EXERCISE 14b

Here are some questions of this kind.

1. Which word tells you what a **plate** always has ?
    (*1*) pattern   (*2*) depth   (*3*) shape   (*4*) colour

2. What does every **cloud** have ?
    (*1*) rain   (*2*) snow   (*3*) colour   (*4*) moisture

3. What do all **books** have ?
    (*1*) pages   (*2*) pictures   (*3*) verses   (*4*) questions

4. What does every **chair** have ?
    (*1*) arms   (*2*) four legs   (*3*) seat   (*4*) sides

5. What does every **loaf of bread** contain ?
    (*1*) crust   (*2*) dough   (*3*) sweetness   (*4*) flour

6. What does every **cupboard** have ?
    (*1*) shelves   (*2*) drawers   (*3*) things in it   (*4*) door

7. What do all **coats** have ?
    (*1*) belts   (*2*) pockets   (*3*) lining   (*4*) seams

8. What do all **babies** have ?
    (*1*) age   (*2*) teeth   (*3*) cots   (*4*) hair

9. What do all **stories** have ?
    (*1*) people   (*2*) events   (*3*) conversation   (*4*) fun

10. What does every **fire** have ?
    (*1*) ashes   (*2*) smoke   (*3*) heat   (*4*) flames

EXERCISE 14c

Think of these :
kettles, saucepans, teapots
What do they all possess ?
spouts, metal bottoms, or handles ?
The answer is **handles.**

Now do ten like that.

1. What do men, dogs and flowers all have ?
   (1) legs   *(2)* life   *(3)* petals   *(4)* eyes
2. What do books, newspapers and posters all possess ?
   (1) paper   *(2)* pages   *(3)* pictures   *(4)* questions
3. What do air-hostesses, policemen and nurses all wear ?
   (1) ties   *(2)* capes   *(3)* helmets   *(4)* uniforms
4. What do shoes, slippers and boots all have ?
   (1) tongues   *(2)* laces   *(3)* toecaps   *(4)* soles
5. What do jumpers, socks and scarves all have ?
   (1) tassels   *(2)* coloured borders *(3)* threads   *(4)* stripes
6. Men, fishes and birds all have what :
   (1) legs   *(2)* wings   *(3)* bones   *(4)* tails ?
7. Chairs, benches and stools all have what :
   (1) backs   *(2)* arms   *(3)* shape   *(4)* nails ?
8. Flowers, butterflies and babies all have what :
   (1) life   *(2)* legs   *(3)* wings   *(4)* eyes ?
9. Shadows, images and visions all have what :
   (1) life   *(2)* movement   *(3)* form   *(4)* substance ?
10. Hills, houses and telegraph poles all have what :
    (1) wires   *(2)* numbers   *(3)* names   *(4)* height ?

15. REVISION TESTS

TEST I

1. If the word REPORTER were written backwards, which letter would have four other letters after it ?

2. Which word has a meaning similar to LARGE among the following ?
   unique,   huge,   terrific,   incredible.

3. One of the words below is opposite in meaning to GO.   Which is it ?
   depart,   immediately,   home,   straight,   come.

4. Which is the odd one in the following list ?
   book,   magazine,   pamphlet,   ticket,   volume.

5. Write down the number that should come next in the following series.
   36,   27,   19,   12,   6

6. Which is the middle number among the following Roman numbers ?
   XI,   VIII,   XIV,   IV,   IX

7. **Thimble** is to **finger** as **helmet** is to which :
   armour,   hand,   breakfast,   head ?

8. Put the following words into proper order and write down the last word.
   The sing to began birds

9. Why do motor-cars have windscreens ?
   (*1*) For the motorist to see through.
   (*2*) To make the car air-tight.
   (*3*) To keep out wind and rain.
   (*4*) To keep out the noises on the road.
   Which is the answer :   (*1*), (*2*), (*3*) or (*4*) ?

10. John was not at school on Friday last.   He was first absent three days before that. Today is Monday, the 31st May.   When was John first absent ?
    Give the day and the date.

11. The word IMPUDENTLY is used as a key word so that I = 1 ; M = 2 ; P = 3 ; U = 4 ; and so on. What would you think is the price of an article marked N·ET ?

12. Write down the word that is missing in the following sentence
    The more a hen lays the cheaper the . . . are.

13. How many letters are alike in the names of the third and fifth months of the year ?

14. Your story is completely <u>incredible.</u>
   Which word below has a meaning similar to that of the word underlined ?
   Is it : (a) insensible ; (b) unbelievable ; (c) strange ; (d) untrue ?

15. The opposite of STRONG is—which :
   poor, sick, tall, weak or young ?

16. Write down the number of the pattern which is most unlike the other three.

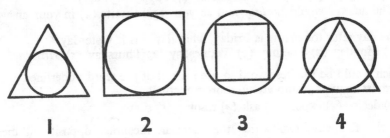

   1   2   3   4

17. Which number ought to come next in this list or series ?
   0, 9, 1, 8, 2, 7

18. Arrange the following in order and then write down the middle date.
   April 20th, May 16th, March 31st, June 2nd, April 4th.

19. A **lift** is to a **staircase** as a **vacuum cleaner** is to
   (1) a dustbin ; (2) a sweeping brush ; (3) a radio ; (4) a refrigerator.
   Which is it : (1), (2), (3) or (4) ?

20. Write down two words in the following mixed-up sentence that should change places to make sense :
   I hear a hammer making a noise with a man.

21. Which sentence, (a), (b), (c) or (d), tells you best what an aeroplane is ?
   (a) A flying device   (c) An air convoy
   (b) A space-ship   (d) An air conveyance.

22. It was foggy yesterday.   Tomorrow is Sunday
   Therefore—
   (a) It is foggy today.
   (b) It will be foggy tomorrow.
   (c) It was foggy on Friday.
   (d) It was foggy on Saturday.
   Which is correct : (a), (b), (c) or (d) ?

23. What have all **houses, flats** and **tea-shops** ?
   Say whether it is **roofs, staircases, walls** or **names.**

24. If four brothers with their wives each with two children met for tea, how many would there be in the party ?
   8, 12, 16, 20, 24 or 40

TEST 2

In this test you are required to write a number for your answer. For example, you might be asked :

What is the opposite of ENERGETIC ?

and you might be given these answers to choose from :

(*1*) hungry (*2*) lazy (*3*) excitable (*4*) happy (*5*) ugly

The answer would be *lazy* and so you would write (*2*) in your answer.

1. If the day after tomorrow is Friday, what day was it yesterday ?
   (*1*) Monday (*2*) Tuesday (*3*) Wednesday (*4*) Thursday (*5*) Saturday

2. Which would be the best word to use instead of the word underlined ?
   I must request you to attend more punctually.
   (*1*) desire (*2*) expect (*3*) ask (*4*) resolve (*5*) pray

3. Are the following two words the same in meaning, opposite in meaning, or neither the same nor opposite ?
   RICH CAREFREE
   (*1*) same (*2*) opposite (*3*) neither

4. Which goes best with PETROL, COKE and COAL ?
   (*1*) Garage (*2*) Miner (*3*) Stove (*4*) Oil (*5*) Rubber

5. Which number comes next in the following series ?
   3, 4, 5, 4, 5, 6, 5, 6, 7
   (*1*) 2 (*2*) 5 (*3*) 8 (*4*) 7 (*5*) 6

6. Find the word which you would place between COARSE and FINE.
   (*1*) Loud (*2*) Proper (*3*) Round (*4*) Medium (*5*) Little

7. Take the smallest odd number which is less than 21 from the smallest even number less than 21. What is the answer ?
   (*1*) 1 (*2*) 2 (*3*) 3 (*4*) 4 (*5*) 5

8. When the following words have been re-arranged to make sense, which is the second word ?
   much big as means same large the
   (*1*) (*2*) (*3*) (*4*) (*5*) (*6*) (*7*)

9. Which tells you best what a **watch** is ?
   (*1*) It gives you the time.
   (*2*) It is a small clock.
   (*3*) You look at it when you want to know the time.
   (*4*) It tells the time and can be carried on the wrist or in the pocket.

10. What number, if doubled, gives you a quarter of 24 ?
    (*1*) 2 (*2*) 3 (*3*) 4 (*4*) 5 (*5*) 6

11. What do all windows have ?
    (1) Curtains (2) Blinds (3) Bolts (4) Glass (5) Sash-cords

12. I walk 12 kilometres to the north, then 10 kilometres east and then 12 kilometres south. How far am I then from my starting point ?
    (1) 8 kilometres (2) 10 kilometres (3) 12 kilometres (4) 9 kilometres

13. What are the three middle letters of the second day after Monday ?
    (1) ESD (2) NES (3) URS (4) UND (5) TUR

14. Which tells you best what a **cellar** is ?
    (1) A room in a house.
    (2) A dark room in a house.
    (3) A room in the basement without windows.
    (4) A room below the level of the ground.

15. *Arrival* is the opposite of :
    (1) Embarkation (2) Appearance (3) Departure (4) Expectation.

16. *Elegant* means :
    (1) Graceful (2) Leggy (3) Careful (4) Prim (5) Proper.

17. What number comes next in this series ?
    10, 5, 12, 6, 14, 7
    (1) 8 (2) 10 (3) 12 (4) 14 (5) 16

18. A class of boys stand in a long line. One boy is 19th in order from both ends. How many boys are there in the class ?
    (1) 19 (2) 38 (3) 36 (4) 37 (5) 40.

19. **Matches** are to a **Matchbox** as **Books** are to :
    (1) Readers (2) Covers (3) a Printer (4) a Library.

20. Which two words in the following sentence ought to change places to make sense ?
    In England the cuckoo comes to April
    (1)   (2)   (3)   (4)   (5)   (6)   (7)

21. Why are people in hot countries advised sometimes to wear dark glasses ?
    (1) It makes them look smarter.
    (2) It keeps insects from their eyes.
    (3) Bright sunlight tires the eyes.
    (4) It makes the world look a pleasanter place.

22. What must I divide 100 by to get half a score ?
    (1) 5 (2) 10 (3) 20 (4) 25 (5) 50.

23. In a foreign language *kara dali deto* means *lovely fresh oranges* ; *kara bali* means *poor oranges* ; and *shri deto* means *fresh lemons*. Which word means *fresh* ?
    (1) kara (2) dali (3) deto (4) bali (5) shri

24. Which of the following words comes first in the dictionary ?
    (1) merit (2) measles (3) miracle (4) mire (5) mere

49

TEST 3

1.—Take 27 from 36. If your answer is an *odd* number write it down as a word. If it is *even* write it as a figure.

2. Which word has the same meaning as *resolute* ?
   Visitor, resident, determined, answered, solved.

3. What is the opposite of *earn* ?
   money, save, spend, use, invest.

4. Which of the following is most unlike the others ?
   doctor, lawyer, professor, carpenter, judge.

5. One number is wrong in the list that follows. Which is it ?
   2, 5, 9, 13, 20, 27

6. Which of these comes in the middle ?
   foot, head, knee, chest, hip.

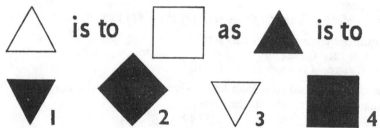

7. Which is it ? 1, 2, 3 or 4

8. If the following words were re-arranged to make a good sentence, with what letter would the last word begin ?
   bricks usually of houses made are

9. We use hot water when washing because :
   (*a*) It loosens dirt better.   (*c*) It feels nicer.
   (*b*) It is better for the hands.   (*d*) It is cheaper than cold water.
   Write (*a*), (*b*), (*c*) or (*d*) for your answer.

10. John has more postage stamps than Jack but not so many as Joe.
    Who has the fewest postage stamps ?

11. What do all shoes have ? Say which it is :
    laces, tongues, soles or leather tops.

12. A man can run 15 kilometres in an hour but he can walk only five. How long will it take him to go 45 kilometres if he runs half the way and walks the rest ?
    Is it 3 hr., $4\frac{1}{2}$ hr., 6 hr., $7\frac{1}{2}$ hr. or 8 hr. ?

13. Which of the following words is the name given to the four other things mentioned ?
    salmon, herring, fish, plaice, cod.

14. Write down the number that comes next in this list :

9, 8, 8, 8, 7, 8, 6

15. Chapter, word, book, paragraph, sentence. Put these in order and write down the one you think should be in the middle.

16. Write the numbers of the two words in the brackets that go together in the same way as the two words at the beginning of the line.

Speech—hear : (picture, concert, feel, speak, see, music)

         1   2   3   4   5   6

17. The following words can be re-arranged to make good sense IF one more word from those in the brackets is added. Which is it ?

The sky in sun summer in the than rises in higher

(clouds, daylight, winter, night-time, eclipse)

18. Write (a), (b), (c) or (d) to show which you think is the best reason for travelling by air.

(a) It is more exciting than travelling by land or water.

(b) It is healthier to be up in the clear air.

(c) It is speedier for long journeys.

(d) It is the latest way.

19. Harry can run 200 metres while Tom runs 120. How many metres ought Tom to be able to run while Harry runs 150 ?

Is it : 80, 90, 100, 110 or 120 ?

20. What does every church tower have ?

(a) a clock (b) a bell (c) a flag (d) height

21. In a certain secret code CALL THE POLICE is written as GEPP XLI TSPMGI. In the same code write CATCH THE APE.

22.

23. Which is the odd shape below ?

24. Find two words that are opposite in meaning in the following list.

(1) Timid (2) Honest (3) Selfish (4) Courageous (5) Handsome.

TEST 4

In working this test you must write down the *number* of the right answer and not the answer itself.

Example

Which part of your foot is nearest the ground when you walk?
(*1*) Ankle   (*2*) Instep   (*3*) Sole   (*4*) Arch.   The answer is (*3*).

1. The sum of all the numbers from 1 to 12 inclusive is :
    (*1*) 60   (*2*) 72   (*3*) 78   (*4*) 84   (*5*) 66

2. Which of the things named below is most like a box, a bag and a bottle?
    (*1*) a table ;   (*2*) a pocket ;   (*3*) a cover ;   (*4*) a sofa ;   (*5*) a mirror

3. Find the word which has the same meaning as the phrase underlined below :
    As a matter of fact the ball was given to me.
    (*1*) Truly   (*2*) Probably   (*3*) Definitely   (*4*) Actually   (*5*) Secretly

4. Which word is out of place in this list?
    (*1*) chase   (*2*) pursue   (*3*) follow   (*4*) stop   (*5*) hunt

5. What number comes next in this list?   12, 2, 1, 14, 4, 2, 16
    (*1*) 6   (*2*) 4   (*3*) 8   (*4*) 18   (*5*) 3

6. Tea, Lunch, Supper, Breakfast, Dinner. Arrange these in order. Which should come last?
    (*1*) Tea   (*2*) Lunch   (*3*) Supper   (*4*) Dinner   (*5*) Breakfast

7. **Predict** is to **Foretell** as **Joy** is to :
    (*1*) Sorrow   (*2*) Happiness   (*3*) Future   (*4*) Past.

8. Re-arrange the following. They will make sense if one more word is added. Which is it?   week is the day of the last.
    (*1*) Monday   (*2*) Saturday   (*3*) Friday   (*4*) Thursday   (*5*) Sunday

9. Why are factory chimneys made tall?
    (*1*) They make the factory more noticeable.
    (*2*) They make a good draught for the factory fires.
    (*3*) They show how busy the factory is.
    (*4*) They give work to steeplejacks.

10. I have three bags of coloured marbles, red, blue, yellow and green. There are as many colours in the first bag as in the second, but the second has a colour which is not in the first. The third bag has one colour and it is in neither of the other bags. If I want to keep as many colours as possible, which bag can I give away?
    (*1*) the first   (*2*) the second   (*3*) the third   (*4*) none of them

11. In a certain code the words COME AT ONCE were written as XLNV ZG LMXV. In the same code which of the following would be O.K.?
    (*1*) LP   (*2*) MP   (*3*) LM   (*4*) KL   (*5*) KM

12. *Too many cooks spoil the broth.* This means :
    (1) Many hands make light work.
    (2) A stitch in time saves nine.
    (3) It doesn't do for several people to interfere in a job that is being done.
    (4) The more people there are in a crowd the more likely it is that there will be trouble.

13. There are four brothers each with a wife who has two sisters. Each person has two children. How many children are there altogether ?
    (1) 3   (2) 24   (3) 9   (4) 12

14. In the alphabet, which letter precedes the letter that comes after M ?
    (1) J   (2) K   (3) L   (4) M   (5) N

15. The opposite of an OPPONENT is :
    (1) An adversary   (2) An enemy   (3) An ally   (4) A neutral

16. *A stitch in time saves nine* means :
    (1) One big stitch is as good as nine small stitches.
    (2) See to things that begin to go wrong before they get too bad.
    (3) Nine children may be saved by one clever person.
    (4) Good sewing makes garments last longer.

17. Which word is out of place in this list of things that are meant to be alike in some way ?   (1) Battle-axe   (2) Spear   (3) Dart   (4) Sword   (5) Cutlass

18. **Mouse** is to **Mice** as **One** is to :
    (1) All   (2) None   (3) Many   (4) More

19. Which number should come next in the series : 1, 4, 3, 8, 5, 12, 7 ?
    (1) 10   (2) 13   (3) 16   (4) 19   (5) 22

20. One of the following tells you best what a **house** is. Which is it ?
    (1) A building made for living in.
    (2) A building with rooms in it.
    (3) A building with a kitchen in it.
    (4) A building with a front door and windows in it.

21. I stand at attention facing the south. My feet do not point exactly straight-forward. Which way do you think my left foot points ?
    (1) West   (2) East   (3) South-west   (4) South-east   (5) North

22. Which TWO sentences of the first four make (5) true ?
    (1) June this year began on a Tuesday.
    (2) Today is the 21st June.
    (3) Two days ago it was Wednesday.
    (4) The 15th June was on a Wednesday.
    Therefore : (5) Today is Monday.

23. If three-tenths of a sum of money is 15p, what is the total sum ?
    (1) 20p   (2) £1·00   (3) 60p   (4) 50p.

24. When Tom was cycling to town he met a man, his wife, two children and a dog. How many more legs than Tom had did he see on his way ?
    (1) 2   (2) 4   (3) 6   (4) 8   (5) 10

TEST 5

1. Which word in the list below tells you what kind of thing the others are ?
   (*1*) Flat   (*2*) House   (*3*) Dwelling   (*4*) Palace   (*5*) Bungalow

2. A O F X B O G X C O . . .
   What letter comes next in the line above ?
   (*1*) D   (*2*) O   (*3*) H   (*4*) X

3. Which word would come best between PAST and FUTURE ?
   (*1*) Yesterday   (*2*) Tomorrow   (*3*) Today   (*4*) Never

4. A **ruler** is to **length** as a **clock** is to :
   (*1*) Minutes   (*2*) Hours   (*3*) Time   (*4*) Future   (*5*) Present

5. Re-arrange the following and add one of the words below to finish the sentence :
   the child is able to older the he ought to be a higher
   (*1*) know   (*2*) feel   (*3*) reach   (*4*) find   (*5*) swim

6. Which tells you best what **bacon** is ?
   (*1*) It is a kind of meat.
   (*2*) It is made from pig-meat.
   (*3*) It is sometimes streaky, sometimes not.
   (*4*) It is prepared by treating pork in a certain way.

7. Mary is 16.   In four years time she will be twice as old as Jane was a year ago. How old is Jane ?
   (*1*) 7   (*2*) 8   (*3*) 9   (*4*) 10   (*5*) 11

8. Many traders prefer to send their goods by lorry instead of by train because :
   (*1*) Lorries travel faster than trains.
   (*2*) Goods can be delivered from door to door without loading and unloading.
   (*3*) Lorries are cheaper to run.
   (*4*) Traders can advertise their goods better by having their names on lorries.

9. A coat always has :
   (*1*) A lining   (*2*) Sleeves   (*3*) Buttons   (*4*) A belt   (*5*) Cuffs

10. Add together every 7 that comes immediately before a 9 below :
    9 7 2 7 9 7 2 9 7 9 2 7 9 2 7
    Which is the answer ?   (*1*) 14   (*2*) 21   (*3*) 28   (*4*) 35   (*5*) 42

11. **Conspicuous** means :
    (*1*) clever   (*2*) outstanding   (*3*) special   (*4*) considerate   (*5*) clear

12. The opposite of **sensitive** is :
    (*1*) cunning   (*2*) conceited   (*3*) thick-skinned   (*4*) ardent
    (*5*) truthful

13. Which number is out of place in the following series ?

    1, 3, 7, 15, 30, 63
   (1) (2) (3) (4) (5) (6)

14. Put these words into proper order and write down the number of the middle one.

    (1) Electric light (2) Flaming torch (3) Oil lamp (4) Candle (5) Gaslight.

15. **Go** is to **went** as **today** is to :

    (1) Yesterday (2) Tomorrow (3) Coming (4) Travel (5) Going

16. Put the following words in sensible order and add one more word to finish the sentence.

    who an play persons of musical consists orchestra

    (1) concerts (2) instruments (3) bands (4) scales (5) audiences

17. Things made of gold cost more than things made of iron because :

    (1) Gold is not so cheap as iron.
    (2) Gold is not so easily melted as iron.
    (3) Gold is more difficult to work with than iron.
    (4) Gold is a rarer metal than iron.

18. Mary and Molly are tall.
Molly and Jane are fair.
Jane and Sally are handsome.
Sally and Molly are dark.
Which of the following is true ?

    (1) Mary and Jane are tall and dark.
    (2) Molly and Sally are handsome and fair.
    (3) Jane is fair and handsome.
    (4) Mary is tall and fair.

19. To say that flowers feel the cold is :

    (1) true (2) absurd (3) intelligent (4) unjust (5) unwise

20. John sits on the right of Jack. Jack sits between Tom and Harry. Who sits farthest to the right ?

    (1) John (2) Jack (3) Tom (4) Harry

21. Choose and write down the word that goes best with *always, never, sometimes.*
Is it yesterday, tomorrow, seldom or today ?

22. Write down the middle even number between 12 and 24.

23. John was a **zealous** supporter of the club.
Find the word that means **zealous** below.

    enthusiastic, downright, open, secret, wealthy

24. Which word means the opposite of **desire** ?

    disgust, pleasure, pain, contentment, hunger

TEST 6

1. Find the four letters that come together and make a word in
   P O A C H E R

2. Which words could you use instead of **inserted** in the sentence :
   A full stop should be **inserted** here.
   (*1*) put up   (*2*) put down   (*3*) put out   (*4*) put in   (*5*) put over

3. What a **peculiar** thing !   **Peculiar** means :
   (*1*) funny   (*2*) strange   (*3*) stupid   (*4*) nice

4. The word that goes best with MOTHER, AUNT, SISTER, is :
   (*1*) father   (*2*) uncle   (*3*) brother   (*4*) niece   (*5*) cousin

5. A number is wrong in the following.   Which is it ?
   64,   49,   37,   25,   16

6. Which of the following comes third in the dictionary ?
   (*1*) measles   (*2*) meals   (*3*) medals   (*4*) marbles   (*5*) metals

7. Which tells you best what a **pen** is ?
   (*1*) An instrument for writing with.
   (*2*) An instrument for dipping into ink.
   (*3*) An instrument that carries ink for writing.
   (*4*) An instrument for writing with ink.

8. What do all **cups, jugs** and **saucepans** have ?
   (*1*) handles   (*2*) spouts   (*3*) lids   (*4*) saucers

9. Mary is a cook.   All cooks are plump.   If this is true, is Mary plump ?
   (*1*) Yes   (*2*) No   (*3*) No one can say.

10. My house faces south-east.   The side door on the right as you approach the front
    of the house therefore faces :
    (*1*) North-east   (*2*) North-west   (*3*) South-west   (*4*) East   (*5*) South

11. If KEGU means ICES then PWV means :
    (*1*) pen   (*2*) nut   (*3*) log   (*4*) cup   (*5*) sun

12. I like to play with Tom and Dick.   Tom and Harry do not like playing with me.
    Who is my friend ?
    (*1*) Tom   (*2*) Dick   (*3*) Harry

13. What do we call the space made by the hands of the clock at three o'clock and nine
    o'clock ?
    (*1*) A square   (*2*) An acute angle   (*3*) A rectangle   (*4*) A right angle

56

14. The numbers on the 30 houses in a street go down on one side and come back on the other, so that No. 1 is opposite No. 30. Which house is opposite to No. 7 ?

    (1) No. 22   *(2)* No. 23   *(3)* No. 24   *(4)* No. 25   *(5)* No. 26

15. **Temporary entrance** means :

    (1) Way in for the time being.
    (2) Way in if you are early.
    (3) Way in if you are now working here.
    (4) Way in now that work is finished.

16. Which goes best with **bacon, ham** and **pork** ?

    (1) margarine   *(2)* butter   *(3)* lard   *(4)* fat

17. L   5   O   M   7   O   N   9.   What comes next ?

    (1) O   P   *(2)* O   O   *(3)* O   Q   *(4)* O   R

18. If the following were arranged in order, which would come in the middle ?

    (1) Christmas   *(2)* Midsummer   *(3)* Whitsuntide   *(4)* New Year's Day
    (5) Easter

19. **Hand** is to **handle** as **foot** is to :

    (1) floor   *(2)* pedal   *(3)* shoe   *(4)* ankle   *(5)* step

20. Why does traffic **keep to the left** in this country ?

    (1) It is the natural thing for it to do.
    (2) It is because there is more room on the left.
    (3) It causes fewer accidents on the left than on the right.
    (4) It is to make movement easier.

21. Re-arrange the following words and choose one to add to make sense :

    like   during   weather   the   be   to   we   good
    (1) yesterday   *(2)* always   *(3)* holidays   *(4)* storms

22. Tom likes ices but not bananas. Mary dislikes apples and chocolates. Sarah likes them all. She invites Tom and Mary to a party. What will she provide for them ?

    (1) Ices   *(2)* Bananas   *(3)* Apples   *(4)* Chocolates

23. Which two statements tell you that it rained yesterday ?

    (1) Today is Sunday.
    (2) It is raining today.
    (3) It rained on Saturday.
    (4) It rained the day before yesterday.

24. Three-fifths of a sum of money is £0·60. What is that sum of money ?

    (1) £0·75   *(2)* £0·40   *(3)* £1·00   *(4)* £10·60   *(5)* £0·80.

TEST 7

1. If six is the half of nine, write " Yes " ; if it is not, write " No ".

2. A word beginning with the letter " I " means the opposite of POLITE.   What is it ?

3. Which two words mean the same in the following list ?
   graceful,   desirable,   praiseworthy,   elegant,   costly

4. **Body** is to **limb** as **tree** is to which—bush, blossom, twig or trunk ?

5. Which is the odd one in the following list ?
   Breeze,   Squall,   Gale,   Hurricane,   Downpour

6. Write down the two numbers that should come next in this series :
   2,   4,   4,   8,   8,   16

7. Arrange the following in order of size and then write down which you have put in the middle.
   $\frac{1}{2}$, $\frac{3}{4}$, $\frac{2}{3}$, $\frac{1}{4}$, $\frac{1}{3}$

8. What do all **fires** have : fuel,   ashes,   smoke,   heat   or   flames ?

9. Which tells you best what a **balcony** is ?
   (a) A shaded part outside a house.
   (b) A railed off part of the outside of a house.
   (c) A railed off part of the outside of a house above street level.
   (d) A verandah.
   Write (a), (b), (c) or (d) to show what you think.

10. Why should we breathe through our noses ?   Write (a), (b), (c) or (d) to show the best answer.
    (a) It makes a better exercise for the chest muscles.
    (b) It helps us to keep our mouths from gaping, which makes us look silly.
    (c) It is the only way of breathing deeply.
    (d) It is the healthiest way of breathing.

11. A shopkeeper uses the word PURCHASING instead of the figures 1 2 3 4 5 6 7 8 9 10.   He wanted to mark an article for sale at £1·25.   What did he put on it as his secret mark ?

12. Try to re-arrange the following words to make a good sentence.   You will find you need one more word.   Write this word down.
    last   year   the   is   of   the   month

13. (a) Barbers use razors in their work.
    (b) John Smith uses a razor in his work.
    (c) John Smith must therefore be a barber.
    Is the third sentence TRUE, FALSE or YOU CAN'T TELL ?

14. Write down the number that should come next in the following series :

    10, 11, 13, 16, 20, 25

15. Sergeant, private, lieutenant, corporal, captain
    Write down the middle one of these after arranging them in order of their rank.

16. The **first** pattern is to the **second** as the **second** is to 1, 2, 3 or 4. Which is it ?

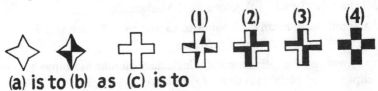

(1)   (2)   (3)   (4)

(a) is to (b) as (c) is to

17. If the following words were re-arranged to make a good sentence, which would be the middle word ?

    the helped beds make I mother my

18. Cotton clothes rather than woollen clothes are worn in hot countries because :
    (a) They are cooler than woollen clothes.
    (b) They last longer.
    (c) They can take prettier dyes.
    (d) They are nicer to look at.
    Write (a), (b), (c) or (d) for the answer.

19. Mary is tall and dark. Molly is short and fair. Milly is fair and tall. Maggie is dark and short. What is the difference between Mary and Milly ?
    Both are . . . but Mary is . . . than Milly.

20. What do all baths have ? Say whether it is soap, water, taps or shape.

21. Continue the series by adding one more word :

    SEAT, TEAS, TALE, LATE, LIFE

22. Which of the following statements is true ?
    (a) X is in the triangle and the square.
    (b) Y is in the triangle and the square.
    (c) Z is in the triangle and the square.
    Write (a), (b) or (c).

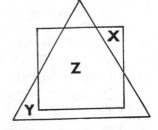

23. He was lucky in finding his audience an **appreciative** one.
    Appreciative means which of the following ?
    Easy, quiet, approving, likeable.

24. The opposite of LOSE is :
    Acquire, accept, invest, borrow, sell ?

59

TEST 8

In working this test you must write down the *number* of the right answer and not the answer itself.

1. Which of the following words will look the same if you write it in capital letters and hold it up to the mirror ?
   (*1*) Minim   (*2*) Level   (*3*) Avova   (*4*) Madam

2. One of the following means the opposite to NOT IN.   Which is it ?
   (*1*) Out   (*2*) In   (*3*) Away   (*4*) Absent

3. Find two words in the following list which have similar meanings :
   (*1*) eclipsed   (*2*) plain   (*3*) dull   (*4*) hidden   (*5*) bright

4. Which would you say is the odd one among these ?
   (*1*) plate   (*2*) saucer   (*3*) tray   (*4*) cup   (*5*) teapot stand

5. Books, newspapers, magazines always have—What ?
   (*1*) Words   (*2*) Pictures   (*3*) Poems   (*4*) Stories   (*5*) Crosswords

6. **Motor car** is to **road** as **ship** is to :
   (*1*) Wave   (*2*) Water   (*3*) Steam   (*4*) Sails   (*5*) Rudder

7. What should come next in the following series : MILLIMETRE, CENTIMETRE, DECIMETRE?
   Is it: (*1*) Hectometre   (*2*) Decametre   (*3*) Metre   (*4*) Kilometre ?

8. When the following words have been put into the order that will make a good sentence, which is the last word ?
   (*1*) make   (*2*) hands   (*3*) light   (*4*) many   (*5*) work

9. If you arrange the following in order, which should be placed in the middle ?
   (*1*) Attic   (*2*) Cellar   (*3*) Ground Floor   (*4*) First Floor   (*5*) Bedroom

10. Which tells you best what **cloth** is ?
    (*1*) Material of which every kind of clothes can be made.
    (*2*) Substance that can be made into clothes.
    (*3*) Material made of threads of wool, cotton, etc., woven closely together.
    (*4*) A coloured patterned material bought in shops.

11. An **opportunity** is :
    (*1*) an event   (*2*) a chance   (*3*) a bit of luck   (*4*) an accident

12. A boy sits in the middle desk in his classroom in a square of desks.   There are three boys to the right of him, three to the left of him, three behind him and three in front of him.   How many boys are there in his class ?
    (*1*) 36   (*2*) 40   (*3*) 45   (*4*) 49   (*5*) 64

13. If I face the setting sun and stretch my right arm sideways, in which direction do you think it would point ?
    (*1*) North   (*2*) South   (*3*) East   (*4*) West

14. John and Mary are blonde and tall. Pat and Sally are dark and short. Harry and Jane are neither blonde nor short. How many of these six are tall ?

     (*1*) 1   (*2*) 2   (*3*) 3   (*4*) 4   (*5*) 5   (*6*) 6

15.

16. Which of the following words comes *last* in the dictionary ?

     (*1*) rich   (*2*) rigid   (*3*) rice   (*4*) rift   (*5*) right

17. Find two sentences in the following that are the same in meaning.

     (*1*) A man is known by the kind of friends he has.
     (*2*) A boy's best friend is his mother.
     (*3*) Don't get into bad company.
     (*4*) Birds of a feather flock together.

18. Which of the following is the odd one ?

     (*1*) Thames   (*2*) Nile   (*3*) Severn   (*4*) Ouse   (*5*) Pacific

19. 142857, 428571, 285714, 857142

     The number that should come next is :

     (*1*) 587142   (*2*) 542871   (*3*) 571428   (*4*) 517428

20. If three-tenths is the half of three-fifths and three-fifths of £1·00 is £0·60, what is £$\frac{3}{10}$?

     (*1*) £0·40   (*2*) £0·30   (*3*) £0·70   (*4*) £0·50   (*5*) £0·25.

21. **Nectar** is to **bee** as **nut** is to :

     (*1*) Nut tree   (*2*) Blackbird   (*3*) Rabbit   (*4*) Squirrel

22. Which of the following is opposite in direction to **South-west** ?

     (*1*) South-east   (*2*) North-east   (*3*) North-west   (*4*) South   (*5*) West

23. Find the word needed to complete this sentence :

     In winter the days get shorter and the nights . . . .

     (*1*) darker   (*2*) quieter   (*3*) longer   (*4*) curtailed   (*5*) brighter

24. Why do people carry watches about with them ?

     (*1*) Because it is safer to have them in their pockets.
     (*2*) It is pleasant to look at them occasionally.
     (*3*) It is useful to know the time wherever you are.
     (*4*) It is something to be able to sell when you are short of money.

TEST 9

In this test the answers required are either figures or letters and NOT words.

1. Which word has the largest number of different letters ?

   (*a*) Marmalade   (*b*) tenacious   (*c*) perpendicular   (*d*) mechanical

2. Pick out the two words in the following list that are opposite in meaning :

   (*a*) Friend   (*b*) scholar   (*c*) pupil   (*d*) foe   (*e*) child

3. The boat was SECURED by means of a rope.   Which of the words below means the same as SECURED ?

   (*1*) Beached   (*2*) landed   (*3*) moved   (*4*) stopped   (*5*) fastened

4. Choose the odd one in this list :

   (*a*) run   (*b*) push   (*c*) pull   (*d*) hoist   (*e*) move

5.

6. What two letters should come next in the following series ?
   X A O W B O V C O
   (*1*) YO   (*2*) UD   (*3*) YD   (*4*) UO

7. Put the following words into the form of a question and then answer it.
   England is largest in the city which
   (*a*) Europe   (*b*) Wales   (*c*) Scotland   (*d*) London

8. Why do farmers keep cows ?

   (*a*) They are easy to look after.   (*c*) They are cheap to feed.
   (*b*) They provide milk for him to use or sell.   (*d*) They keep the grass short.
   Which is the best reason ?

9. John has one sister, Ann, and two brothers, Dick and Alan.   Mary has a brother, Tom, and two sisters, Joan and Jean.
   Who has more brothers than John ?
   (*1*) Ann   (*2*) Dick   (*3*) Alan   (*4*) Tom   (*5*) Joan

10. Who has more sisters than Mary ?

11. Most boys are lively.   Most dull boys are either unhealthy or stupid.   If Tom is dull, then :
    (*1*) He is lively   (*2*) He is stupid   (*3*) He is unhealthy   (*4*) One cannot say.

12. Which of the following should come in the middle when they are properly arranged in order ?
    (*a*) horse   (*b*) dog   (*c*) elephant   (*d*) mouse   (*e*) pig

13. Write the missing word :

MARKET   SAMPLE   FACADE

MART   SAME   . . .

   (a) face (b) fade (c) feed (d) fact.

14. What is the missing number in this square ?

   (1) 18 (2) 27 (3) 36 (4) 81

2	4	16
3	9	
4	16	256

15. Which sentence below tells you best what a **beard** is ?

   (1) A hairy covering over a man's face.

   (2) A hairy covering over a man's mouth.

   (3) A hairy growth on a man's chin and cheeks.

   (4) A hairy growth on a man's head and face.

16. What do the following all have ?

JAM,   HONEY,   TREACLE,   SUGAR

   (a) Pips (b) colour (c) sweetness (d) stickiness

17. Which is the odd one in this list ?

   (1) Gold (2) Bronze (3) Silver (4) Marble (5) Copper

18. I was aware that I had seen him as an actor.

Which of the following words could you use instead of those underlined above ?

   (1) noticed (2) accepted (3) recognised (4) received

19. 1, 17, 33, 49, 65, . . .

What number ought to come next ?

   (a) 85 (b) 80 (c) 82 (d) 81

20. Which of the four shapes, a, b, c or d, goes best with the first three ?

21. Re-arrange the following to make a sensible sentence and then write down the number of the last word in it.

   made   in   armchairs   sitting   for   are

   (1)   (2)   (3)   (4)   (5)   (6)

22. **Piano** is to **fingers** as **trumpet** is to :

   (1) solo (2) blow (3) breath (4) lips (5) hands

23. Most people have bacon for breakfast because :

   (a) They like it.

   (b) It is cheaper than anything else.

   (c) There is plenty of it in the shops.

   (d) It is easy to cook.

24. Mary and Jane are both clever. Jean and Jane are tall. Mary and Jean are both dark. My friend is tall and clever. Who is she ?

   (a) Mary (b) Jane (c) Jean (d) I cannot say.

TEST 10

1. Which word is out of place in this list ?
   man, boy, youth, lad, child.

2. A D O B E O C F O D
   Write down the two letters that should come next.

3. BUNGALOW, HUT, LOG–CABIN, PALACE, HOUSE
   Which of these is likely to be the largest but one ?

4. A **church** is to a **congregation** as a **house** is to—which ?
   (*1*) a family   (*2*) a street   (*3*) rooms   (*4*) a landlord
   Write the number of the right answer.

5. The following words can be re-arranged to make a good sentence. What, then,
   would be the first letter of the last word ?
   pin   me   could   drop   you   a   hear

6. Why do we have clocks that strike the hour ?
   (*a*) For the benefit of blind people.
   (*b*) To remind us of the time when we cannot see them.
   (*c*) Because of their pleasant sound.
   (*d*) To keep us awake.
   Write (*a*), (*b*), (*c*) or (*d*) for the best answer.

7. John is taller than James. Joseph is taller than John. James is shorter than
   Joseph.
   If the first two sentences state the facts, say whether the third is :
   (*a*) true   (*b*) false   (*c*) one cannot say

8. **Export** means to carry or take out.
   Exhale means breathe out.
   Therefore ex- means—which ?
   (*a*) out   (*b*) carry   (*c*) breathe   (*d*) take

9. Which of the following words *cannot* be made from the letters in the word
   MACHINERY ?
   chain,   charm,   cream,   rich,   reach,   catch

10. Write in capital letters in reverse (or backward) order the name HERCULES.

11. My reputation is at stake.
    (*a*) I shall have to pay for this.
    (*b*) I am in danger of losing my good name.
    (*c*) I shall probably lose a great deal of money.
    (*d*) I am in deadly peril.
    Which sentence means the same as the first : (*a*), (*b*), (*c*) or (*d*) ?

12. Which word has the opposite meaning to that of **generous** ?
particular, extravagant, special, loving, mean

13. Write down the middle letter of :
THE MEDITERRANEAN SEA

14. Which of the following words has a meaning opposite to **always** ?
sometimes, frequently, never, often

15. Which of the following words or phrases has nearly the same meaning as **seldom** ?
once a week, rarely, never, sometimes

16. Write down the name of the thing which is out of place among the following :
Potato Poppy Rose Dandelion Daisy

17. Re-arrange the following sentence to make sense, and then write down the last word of it :
school learns in books a read child to

18. Give a good reason for thinking the following statement either sensible or absurd.
If the sun shines all day we shall get rain.

19. Which is the best of the reasons given below **why mothers feed their babies on milk,** (a), (b), (c) or (d) ?
Because : (a) it is sold in bottles ;
(b) it can be kept fresh ;
(c) it is a good food for babies ;
(d) it contains a rich cream.

20. Give two good reasons for thinking the following statement a silly one :
There have been no inventions since 1960, and even in 1966 there was only one.

21. Bristol is bigger than Bath but not so big as Birmingham.
Write down the name of the smallest of these towns.

22. **Right** is to **left** as **below** is to what ?
ground, ceiling, above, underneath

23. What name do we give to things like coal, iron, copper, lead :
rocks, metals, minerals, alloys ?

24. What do all plants have :
smell, seeds, green leaves stems ?

TEST II

1. Look at the numbers that follow and write down which two numbers should come next :

    1, 2, 4, 7, 11, 16

2. My birthday is on New Year's Day. My cousin is three days younger than I am. When does his birthday come ?

3. Arrange the following in order of size. Then write down what comes in the middle :

    short, gigantic, miniature, average, tall

4. Arrange the following in order (simplest first) and make drawings of each :

    triangle, line, oblong, angle

5. Make a drawing of the shape that must be added to this :

    to make a rectangle like this :

6. In secret writing VJG GPGOA KU KP UKIJV means THE ENEMY IS IN SIGHT. What do you think the following means ?

    VJGA UGG OG

7. Half a loaf is better than no bread, means—which of the following, (a), (b), (c) or (d) ?

    (a) A little is better than nothing at all.
    (b) The first half of a loaf is usually the better half.
    (c) Cake is better than stale bread.
    (d) No bread is as good as this half-loaf.

8. Begin the following sentence with one of the words printed in capital letters :

    . . . it is nearly mid-summer we have had few sunny days.

    IF, WHEN, BECAUSE, ALTHOUGH

9. Write down the letters in the word CONSTANTINOPLE which come together twice but in different order.

10. Say whether the following pairs of words are similar or opposite in meaning :

    (a) Expect . . . Anticipate
    (b) Thrilling . . . Exciting

11. Which word in the brackets means nearly the same as HEAT ?

    (fire, thermometer, warmth, temperature)

12. Which of the things named below goes best with **shirt, coat** and **stockings** ?

    handbag, purse, shoes, umbrella

13. The words of the sentence which follows have got mixed up.   Sort them out and write the sentence down as it should be :

    pain   the   greedy   apples   a   sour   the   boy   gave

14. Which word in the following sentence would you change to make sense ?

    When mother does not feel ill she ought to lie down and rest.

15. Which of the following is the best reason for taking exercise ?

    (a) It gives us something to do.
    (b) It uses up our energy.
    (c) It improves our health.
    (d) It is a pleasant change from study.

16. Which of the following seems to you to be most correct ?

    (a) When the yellow light shows, it is a sign that traffic can go ahead.
    (b) We ought to clean our teeth to please our friends.
    (c) Wherever apples grow, bananas will also grow.
    (d) Coal burns better and lasts longer than wood.

17. Gold is heavier than mercury.
    Mercury is heavier than tin.
    Tin is lighter than lead.
    Lead is lighter than mercury.
    When you compare GOLD and LEAD, what then can you say about them ?

18. **Spring** is to **summer** as **breakfast** is to—what ?

    tea,   morning,   luncheon,   getting up

19. Find a single word that will do as a name for :

    carts,   trains,   buses,   bicycles

20. Think of these : **kettles, saucepans, teapots.**   What does each possess ?

    Spouts,   metal-bottoms,   handles.

21. Write down the two numbers which should come next in the following series :

    1,   4,   9,   16,   25.

22. Two of the following sayings seem to have opposite meanings.   Which are they ?

    (a) Too many cooks spoil the broth.
    (b) A rolling stone gathers no moss.
    (c) Many hands make light work.
    (d) It is never too late to mend.

23. Write down the following sentence, leaving out the words in the brackets not needed :

    I went to the (grocer's, chemist's, stationer's) to buy father some (buttons, ink, tobacco).

24. PBZR NG BAPR.   This is a message in code which means COME AT ONCE.   Make a reply in the same code meaning MEET ME AT TEN.

TEST 12

In this test the answers required are either figures or letters and NOT words.

1. Which of the following numbers contains 2, 3, 4, 6 and 8 an exact number of times ?

    (*1*) 8   (*2*) 12   (*3*) 18   (*4*) 24   (*5*) 30   (*6*) 36

2. When an article has a LUSTRE it is :

    (*1*) valuable   (*2*) fragile   (*3*) shiny   (*4*) antique   (*5*) unpolished

3. Mary is taller than Jane, who is of the same height as Irene. Mary therefore is :
    (*1*) taller than Irene   (*2*) shorter than Irene   (*3*) the same as Irene in height
    (*4*) of doubtful height

4. WHEAT   OATS   BARLEY

    Which of the following goes best with the three things above ?

    (*1*) corn   (*2*) hay   (*3*) rye   (*4*) potatoes   (*5*) beans

5. **Come** is to **go** as **arrival** is to :

    (*1*) Airport   (*2*) Departure   (*3*) Disappearance   (*4*) Terminus

6. In hot countries people begin work very early in the morning and rest in the afternoon *because* :
    (*1*) They have to get up early.
    (*2*) They have nothing else to do during the morning.
    (*3*) It is too hot for work in the afternoon.
    (*4*) The shops are not open in the afternoon.

7. John and Joe are very brainy.   Harry and Tom are not very bright.   Joe and Tom work hard at lessons.   Who is likely to be top at the end of the term ?
    (*1*) John   (*2*) Joe   (*3*) Harry   (*4*) Tom

8. Henry has three sisters. Tom has two sisters. Dick has one sister. Which of the sisters has more than one brother ?
    (*1*) Henry's sisters   (*2*) Tom's sisters   (*3*) Dick's sister   (*4*) No one's sisters

9. More than half the boys in my class wear school caps.   More than half the boys in my class wear school ties.   Therefore :
    (*1*) Some boys wear school caps and school blazers.
    (*2*) Some boys wear school caps and school ties.
    (*3*) No boys wear both school ties and school caps.
    (*4*) No boys wear both school ties and school blazers.
    Which is true: (*1*), (*2*), (*3*) or (*4*) ?

10. In a certain kind of secret writing SEND HELP AT ONCE is written as TFOE IFMQ BU PODF.

    Which of the following means YES in this code ?

    (*1*) zdr   (*2*) zft   (*3*) cvo   (*4*) agu

68

11. **Textiles** are :
(*1*) Slates for roofs (*2*) Woven materials (*3*) Study books (*4*) Bible sayings

12. The opposite of **injurious** is :
(*1*) dangerous (*2*) beneficial (*3*) helpful (*4*) violent

13. Harry's father is my mother's brother. What relation is Harrry to me ?
(*1*) brother (*2*) uncle (*3*) nephew (*4*) cousin (*5*) father

14. What letter comes halfway between M and S in the alphabet ?
(*1*) Q (*2*) N (*3*) P (*4*) O (*5*) R

15. If you mix up the letters in MEAL and add another letter you can make the name of an animal. What is it ?
(*1*) Mole (*2*) Mabel (*3*) Medal (*4*) Camel

16. Which is the odd one in the following list ?
(*1*) London (*2*) China (*3*) Canada (*4*) France (*5*) Germany

17. **Decrease** means the same as :
(*1*) grow (*2*) get bigger (*3*) get smaller (*4*) sink

18. Add together the numbers in the triangle but not in the square or the circle, and take away from your answer the sum of the numbers in the square but not in the triangle or circle. What is the answer ?
(*a*) 2 (*b*) 4 (*c*) 6 (*d*) 8 (*e*) 10

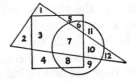

19. vessels usually make empty the noise of biggest
(*1*)   (*2*)   (*3*)   (*4*)   (*5*)   (*6*)   (*7*)   (*8*)
Leave out one word and the rest will make a sentence. Which is the word ?

20. **Father** is to **mother** as **husband** is to :
(*1*) daughter (*2*) sister (*3*) wife (*4*) aunt (*5*) grandmother

21. In a secret way of writing JCXG VQ IQ UWFFGPNA means HAVE TO GO SUDDENLY. What does IF become in this code ?
(*a*) GI (*b*) KI (*c*) GD (*d*) KH (*e*) KG

22. Which number below is most unlike the others ?
(*1*) 203 (*2*) 506 (*3*) 102 (*4*) 608 (*5*) 304

23. All dogs have . . . . What ?
(*1*) fur (*2*) whiskers (*3*) puppies (*4*) legs (*5*) collars

24. There is a saying that *A bird in the hand is worth two in the bush.* This means :
(*a*) The bird you have caught is a good one.
(*b*) The bird you have is as big as the two left.
(*c*) That which you have is worth twice what you may perhaps get.
(*d*) Birds of a feather do not always flock together.

TEST 13

1. Make a word from the three letters which are repeated in :
   ENTERTAINMENT

2. Which of the words in the brackets is opposite in meaning to EXCITED ?
   (recited, decided, placid, placed).

3. Which of the words in the brackets goes best with GRIEF, MISERY, SADNESS ?
   (joy, sorrow, happiness, relief)

4. Which word seems not to belong here ?
   water, beer, lemonade, ink, wine

5. Look at each of the following sets of words. Think what the sentence would be if the words were put in the right order. Then write whether they are *true* or *false*.
   (*a*) January is in Christmas.
   (*b*) Forty-five eleven are fours.

6. Change one of the words in this sentence to make it sensible :
   Food is one of the luxuries of life.

7. Which of the reasons, (*a*), (*b*), (*c*) or (*d*), is needed to make the following statement a sensible one ?
   Children should wash themselves because :
   (*a*) it makes them feel good ;
   (*b*) they will be scolded if they do not ;
   (*c*) it is good for their health ;
   (*d*) it makes them look clever.

8. The following sentence could be made reasonable by the change of a single word. Find the word and write another instead of it.
   I have three sisters, Mary, Jean and myself.

9. **Pears** are dearer than **apples** and **apples** are cheaper than **oranges**. Which are the dearest ?
   Apples, oranges, pears, or can't you tell ?

10.

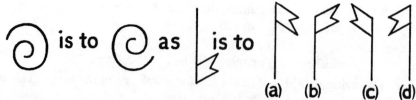

11. (*a*) What name can we give IRON, QUICKSILVER and GOLD ?
    (*b*) Which of these words stands for all the others :
    POTATOES, VEGETABLES, TURNIPS, PEAS ?

12. (a) What do all boys have :
   POCKETS, COATS, MOUTHS, BREAKFAST, BOOTS ?
   (b) What do all shops have :
   GROCERIES, COUNTERS, SCALES, GOODS ?

13. What do you think are the missing numbers in the next line ?
   9, 0, 8, . . . , 7, 2, . . . , 3, 5, 4

14. Arrange the following in order and then write down the middle one *only* :
   town, house, street, country, room

15. A church tower is six-sided. What is the greatest number of sides that can be seen at once ?

16. GREAT is written as FQDZS. How would DANGER be written ?

17. Look at these three proverbs. Two of them mean nearly the opposite of each other. Which is the other one ?
   (a) Unity is strength.
   (b) Too many cooks spoil the broth.
   (c) Absence makes the heart grow fonder.

18. Which word in capitals is needed to begin this sentence ?
   . . . I am unable to come to see you, much as I should like.
   HAPPILY, UNFORTUNATELY, ALTHOUGH, NOTWITHSTANDING

19. Find the two proverbs that are most alike, and write their letters.
   (a) Trouble is not wholly evil.
   (b) Every cloud has a silver lining.
   (c) Laugh today and cry tomorrow.

20. Re-arrange in your head BOYS THAN SEW GIRLS CAN BETTER. Now add any one of the following words which will make sense and write down the sentence.
   ALWAYS, NEVER, USUALLY

21. If A, E, I, O and U were dropped out of the alphabet, which letter would come tenth ?

22. Find the word which means the opposite of MODESTY :
   scorn, luxury, pride, humility

23. Which word in the brackets has a meaning very much like ACCEPT ?
   (except, receive, expect, accede)

24. Which of the following is out of place because it does not go well with the others ?
   rice, sugar, treacle, honey, jam

TEST 14

1. The words in the following sentence are mixed up. Think how they should run. Is what they say *true* or *false* ?

   England is of Edinburgh the capital.

2. Find two words in each sentence below that need to change places to make sense of what is said.

   (a) Tom threw a wall right over the stone.

   (b) Elsie lost a street in the penny.

3. We know iron is heavier than water because :

   (a) Iron ships float in water.

   (b) Water is not solid like iron.

   (c) Bridges are made of iron.

   (d) Iron will sink in water.

   Which is the best reason : (a), (b), (c) or (d) ?

4. Give a reason why the following statement is absurd.

   All the way to the sea and all the way home again the road was uphill.

5. Mary has two brothers, Jack and Tom. They have two cousins, Ellen and Jane. How many cousins at least have Ellen and Jane ?

6.

   Make a drawing of the arrow, (a), (b), (c) or (d), which is in the right position.

7. Find a word or words which will be a name for **men, fishes, birds** and **plants.**

8. Name two things possessed by the following :

   (a) All rivers have (banks, bridges, water, fish, towns) in them.

   (b) All towns have (mayors, houses, cathedrals, streets, factories).

9. Look at the following numbers and add two more which you think should come after them :

   14, 16, 17, 20, 21, 25, 26

10. Arrange the following according to size :

    bee, elephant, mouse, dog, tiger

    Which comes in the middle ?

11. Draw a small square and place a triangle completely inside it.

12. The following is in secret writing. Write down what it means *and answer it.*

    A = N   JUNG NER GJB SBHEF ?

    B = O

13. (a) If a kilo of lead weighs more than a kilo of feathers, write *Yes*. If not, write *No*.

(b) Draw a rectangle and put a small cross in the bottom left-hand corner of it.

14. Which of the words inside the brackets has a meaning opposite to that of the word outside ?

(Rest, exercise, work, play) Recreation.

15. Which of the words in the brackets can have a meaning like that of the first word in the line ?

(a) Fragrant—(volatile, essential, aromatic, ethereal).

(b) Produced—(imported, manufactured, caught, led on).

16. Which word *in* the brackets goes best with those *outside* the brackets ?

(a) Cow, pig, sheep—(Farmer, goat, shepherd, robin).

(b) Apple, plum, pear—(Jam, cider, orange, lettuce).

17. Re-arrange these sentences in your head and then write down whether what they say is *true* or *false*.

(a) Boys disliked selfish usually are.

(b) You than move cars can motor or faster me.

18. You can change over two words in each sentence that follows to make sense. Which are they ?

(a) It is not easy to sell handles without buckets.

(b) Nearly all flowers like children.

19. Why do soldiers wear uniforms ?

(a) To impress the enemy.

(b) To be easily recognised.

(c) To use up army clothing.

Write down the best answer.

20. What is wrong in the sentence below ? Why ?

" Tom and Mary are brother and sister. Tom has two sisters and two brothers, and so has Mary."

21. Wool is dearer than cotton, but not so dear as silk. Write which material is the dearest.

22. **Love** is to **friends** as **hatred** is to what :

parents, enemies, brothers, strangers ?

23. In what way are the following alike ?

Motor-car tyres, ink eraser, uskide soles

24. What do all houses have :

cupboards, chimneys, attics, floors ?

73

TEST 15

1. Add two more to the following set of numbers :
   2, 5, 10, 17, 26

2. Which is the " different " proverb below ?
   (a) Many hands make light work.
   (b) Too many cooks spoil the broth.
   (c) Two heads are better than one.

3. Which three words are not needed in the following statement ?
   Arabs travel/fly from one place to nowhere/another on horseback/camels.

4. Think how these should be arranged :
   Baby, grandfather, father, boy, youth
   Write down which comes in the middle.

5. Onetown is two km north of Twotown.   Twotown is two km east of Threetown.
   In what direction would you travel in going from Onetown to Threetown ?

6. If you write Z for A, Y for B, X for C, etc., how will you write JOHN HAS RETURNED ?

7. Two of the following statements mean nearly the same.   Which is the other one ?
   (a) He who hesitates is lost.
   (b) Nothing venture, nothing win.
   (c) Look before you leap.

8. Supply the words which would best complete this sentence :
   I shall take my umbrella with me . . . it should rain.

9. (a) Which number is in both triangles and the circle ?

   (b) Which number is not in either triangle ?

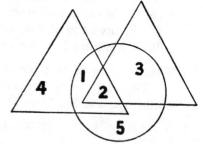

10. Choose and write down two words from the following that are opposite in meaning :
    History, ancient, cinema, up-to-date, English, Briton.

11. Look at the first word in each line below and choose a word to match it from the four that follow it.
    (a) Huge—monstrous, gigantic, horrid, terrific.
    (b) Sympathetic—unkind, personal, kindly, pitiful.

74

12. Two words in the following list name things which are of a different sort from the others. Which are they ?

   England, London, France, Germany, Paris, Spain, Italy

13. Re-arrange these sentences in your head and then write down the last word in each.

   (a) Sea in fishes the live.
   (b) Spoons we eat with soup.

14. Here are some sentences with two words that have changed places in each. Find the two words in each sentence.

   (a) The carpenter hit his head on the nail with a hammer.
   (b) How many times not I told you have to climb trees ?
   (c) I hear him, but could not make him saw my call.

15. Why are shoes made of leather ? Which is the best answer below ?

   (a) Leather is plentiful.
   (b) It wears well.
   (c) It is cheap.
   (d) It takes a nice polish.

16. Would you agree with the following ? Give your reason.

   Safety razors and safety pins are so called because we cannot harm ourselves in using them.

17. (a) John's uncle is Mr. Jones, who has a daughter Annie.
        What relation is John to Annie's mother ?
   (b) Plum cake is dearer than currant cake ; currant cake is cheaper than sultana cake. Which is the dearest ?

18. **Leg** is to **ankle** as **arm** is to what :

   Wrist, elbow, hand or shoulder ?

19. In what way are **cousins, aunts, nephews** and **grandmothers** alike ?

20. What does every CUPBOARD have ?

   Shelves, drawers, things in it, a door

21. Write down the following numbers, and add the two which you think should come next after them :

   2, 5, 10, 17

22. Write down the number of times each of the following letters occurs in the words of question 17 (a) and (b) above :

   A, E, I, O, U

23. Re-arrange the following periods of time in your head. Then write down the middle one :

   Minute, Second, Year, Hour, Week

24. The following is a hidden message, in which only some of the words are to be read. What is the message ?

   " Black Diamond today is not in for the Gold Vase. Sent by John the Young Stable Boy."

75

TEST 16

1. Write down :

   (a) The number which is in the oblong and the circle but not in the triangle.

   (b) The number which is in the triangle and the circle but not in the oblong.

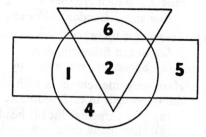

2. Look at the first word below. Which of the four words that follow is opposite in meaning ?

   Seldom—sometimes, often, rarely, always

3. **Lion, cat, tiger.** Which of the following is most like these animals ?
   elephant, kangaroo, leopard

4. Which word names a different sort of thing ?
   table, chair, stool, couch, bed

5. Re-arrange the following statements in your head and say whether they are true.
   (a) Vessels most contain empty water.
   (b) Say between you not must I and he.

6. Find *two words* in the following which must be interchanged if the sentences are to make sense :
   (a) The egg ate the baby.
   (b) The sticky boy ate the little bun.
   (c) Money spend not as easy to earn as it is to is.

7. Why do people take exercise ? Which is the best reason, (a), (b), (c) or (d) ?
   (a) To keep them out of mischief.
   (b) To keep fit and well.
   (c) To win at games.
   (d) To improve their looks.

8. Why is the following silly ?
   There have been no accidents since 1965 and only one occurred in 1966.

9. Which part of a bus travels the faster, the part at the front where the driver sits or the part at the back where the conductor stands ?

10. How shall we finish the following ?
    Preacher is to **sermon** as **teacher** is to (pupil, book, lesson, blackboard).
    Which is the best of the four words in the brackets ?

11. (a) State in what way a **car, a train** and a **ship** are alike.
    (b) State in what way an **onion, a rose** and an **oak tree** are alike.

12. (a) **Men—fishes—birds** all have what :
       backs, arms, bones, tails ?
    (b) **Chairs—benches—stools** all have what :
       backs, arms, seats, legs ?

13. Add two more to each of the following sets of numbers :
    (a) 99, 87, 75, 63, $\cdots$
    (b) 3, 2, 4, 3, 5, 4, 6, $\cdots$

14. What do you notice about the letters in the word CAUCASUS ?

15. Re-arrange the following in your head. Then write down the middle one.
    warm, hot, cold, tepid, boiling

16. A shopkeeper uses the word IMPORTANCE to stand for the figures 1 to 10 so that
    I = 1, M = 3, etc. He marks some goods to be sold for I·RT. What do you
    think this means ?

17. Which is the odd proverb here ?
    (a) Once bitten, twice shy.
    (b) Try before you buy.
    (c) Look before you leap.

18. Choose a word from the brackets to make the sentence read sensibly.
    I went down into the (shop, cellar, cupboard) and brought up a shovelful of
    (snow, coal, water).

19. Which of the following is the odd statement ?
    (a) Misfortunes never come singly.
    (b) It never rains but it pours.
    (c) Every cloud has a silver lining.

20. Which of the words in capitals best completes this sentence :
    I love my mother . . . she is unkind to me.
    WHENEVER, ALTHOUGH, IF

21. (a) Write down in words the number between 1 and 20 that contains nine letters.
    (b) Which letter occurs most often in the answer to (a) ?

22. Find two words among the following that are opposite in meaning :
    clever, ingenious, crafty, stupid, slow

23. **Sad** means the same as which of the following :
    unlucky, unhappy, hurt, lost ?

24. Which of the following seems not to match the others ?
    letter, sentence, word, diagram, syllable

TEST 17

1. The words in the sentence following have been mixed up. Write the sentence as it ought to be.
is dirty drink to water it unsafe.

2. Find two words in each sentence that need to change places to make sense.
(a) Bananas grow hot in countries.
(b) Trees have their ground in the roots.

3. Why do we ventilate rooms ? Which is the best answer, (a), (b), (c) or (d) ?
(a) Windows get stuck fast if not opened sometimes.
(b) It makes a change to see the windows opened.
(c) Warm air is bad for us.
(d) The air in rooms needs to be changed frequently.

4. What is wrong with this statement ?
Jones, Brown and Robinson made a very happy quartette.

5. Tom sits on the right of Jack. Jack sits on the right of Joe. Who sits in the middle ?

6. Find a word in the brackets to complete each statement satisfactorily.
(a) Flower : petal : : Boy : (girl, head, father, house).
(b) Football : kite : : Bread : (peas, trees, stones, cupboard).

7. Say in what way the following are alike :
(a) Smell, touch, hearing.
(b) Pearl, emerald, sapphire.

8. (a) What do all trees have :
fruit, nests, roots, flowers ?
(b) What do all dogs have :
bones to eat, kennels, tongues ?

9. If the following were re-arranged in proper order, which would come in the middle ?
Book, page, chapter, letter, word.

10. Write the word BED as it would appear on a rubber stamp used for printing it.

11. Re-write the following word so that the letters come in the same order as in the alphabet.
UPRIGHT

12. The following contains a message in code. Can you find it ?
Bread 4p, Sugar 5p, Eggs 1p, Pastry 6p, Oranges 1p, Butter 2p, Pears 4p, Apples 5p, Apricots 1p, Dates 1p, Jelly 5p.
Each number tells you something about a letter in the word before it.

13. Two days of the week have the same number of letters. Write the first letter of each name.

14. Look at the first word in each line below. Which word of the four that follow has an opposite meaning ?
    (a) Similar—same, different, off, even.
    (b) Frozen—hard, jelly-like, thawed, liquid.

15. REPAIR means the same as . . . which of the following ?
    Replace, renew, improve, renovate.

16. Find the odd thing mentioned in each line below :
    (a) Apple, pear, cucumber, plum.
    (b) Blackboard, duster, teacher, chalk.
    (c) Flour, sugar, water, salt.

17. Write out two words which must change places in the following sentence if it is to have sense :
    John fish to the river to catch some went.

18. Re-arrange the words below to make a true statement. Which is the last word ?
    Burn wood fires longer than coal.

19. Why are eggs cheapest in the spring : (a), (b), (c) or (d) ?
    (a) We need more eggs in spring.
    (b) Hens lay more eggs in spring.
    (c) People have more money in the spring.
    (d) They do not go bad so quickly in spring.

20. Explain what is wrong with the following sentence :
    John's sister Emily has one brother and so has John.

21. Tom and Dick are good in their behaviour. Harry and John are not good. Dick and Harry are clever.
    (a) Who is clever as well as good ?
    (b) Who is neither good nor clever ?

22. One of the words numbered is needed to complete the following statement. Which is it ?
    Love is to **hate** as **heat** is to . . .
    (1) Burning (2) Cold (3) Warmth (4) Iceberg

23. Which of the things below is most like these three : **coal, wood, coke** ?
    Shovel, peat, poker, gas-stove

24. What do all **knives** have ? Write down the correct answer.
    Forks, points, handles, sharp edges.

TEST 18

1. Which number does not belong to its set of figures ?
   (a) 2, 3, 6, 8, 10, 12.
   (b) 36, 31, 25, 21, 16, 11.

2. In what order would the following words come in a dictionary ? Write them out in this order.
   bread, cheese, apple, plum, banana, peach.

3. A boy looked at the clock and mistook the long hand for the short hand. He thought the time was two and a half minutes past six. What do you think the right time was ?

4. A shopkeeper uses the word EDINBURGH as a code, so that E = 1, D = 2, I = 3, etc. How much do you think he will charge for an article marked DB·EB ?

5. Which statement, (a), (b), (c) or (d), means the same as *Birds of a feather flock together* ?
   (a) Birds will come when food is put out for them.
   (b) Those who want to do the same thing are many.
   (c) The smaller the bird the greater the flock.
   (d) People will usually make friends with others like themselves.

6. Which of the words in capitals is needed to complete the following sentence ?
   Many interesting things have happened . . . we returned to school
   BECAUSE, SINCE, BEFORE, WHILE

7. Print the twelfth letter of the alphabet.

8. Find the word which is the opposite of **suitable.**
   similar, convenient, unsatisfactory, invaluable

9. Which two phrases below are most alike in meaning, (a), (b), (c) or (d) ?
   (a) An unmannerly show of thanklessness.
   (b) An awkward show of pleasure.
   (c) An unpleasing exhibition of ingratitude.
   (d) A sorry spectacle of bad temper.

10. What kind of thing is :
    (a) **An orange ?**
       Plant, seed, fruit, flower, round.
    (b) **Courage ?**
       A weakness, a virtue, an action, a strong man.

11. If two words in the following sentence were to change places, the statement would be a sensible one. Find these two words.
    Some organs play pianos ; some play musicians.

12. Do the words below make a true or a false statement when re-arranged in the right order ?
    Wash John the in his lost crown king

80

13. Which is the best reason for using soap for washing, (a), (b), (c) or (d)?
   (a) It smells nice.
   (b) It makes a lather.
   (c) It removes dirt quickly.
   (d) It softens the water.

14. The ladder just reached the window sill so that in a moment Jack climbed up and jumped off into the bedroom.
   What have you to say about the above sentence? Do you see anything wrong with it?

15. Read the following statements and then give the correct answers to questions (a) and (b). That is, write *Yes* or *No* or *You cannot tell*.
   John is taller than James.
   James is shorter than Harry.
   Harry is taller than Tom.
   (a) Is Tom taller than John?
   (b) Is James taller than Harry?

16. Find two words *inside* the brackets that go with one another in the same way as the two *outside*.
   (a) Hat, head—(Face, leg, foot, glove, mouth, shoe).
   (b) Water, air—(Rest, fish, bird, tree, sea, branch, swim).

17. Which word is most like NIMBLE in meaning?
   (a) Eager (b) Agile (c) Humble (d) Poor (e) Honest

18. Find the word that is opposite in meaning to ADVANCE.
   (a) Pursue (b) Retreat (c) Resign (d) Yield (e) Surrender

19. Which is most like these three : **chair, window-seat, bench?**
   Table, bed, mantelpiece.

20. All **trousers** have what :
   braces, belts, legs, pockets?

21. A number is missing from each row of figures below. What is it?
   (a) 1, 1, 2, 3, 3, 4, 5, . . ., 6.
   (b) 9, 0, 8, 1, 7, . . ., 6, 3, 5, 4.

22. Think of how the following might be put into a good order. Then say which is the middle one.
   Aeroplane, Steam engine, Motor car, Canoe, Sailing ship.

23. Write out the word below which is most like **coarse** in its meaning.
   course, refined, rough, smooth

24. In secret writing COME is written as XLNV and ABLE as ZYOV. How would you write MOLLY in the same secret writing?

TEST 19

1. If the first three letters were left out of the alphabet, what would be the eighth letter ?

2. Write down the two words in the following list which have opposite meanings :
   bright,   distinct,   vague,   shining,   queer.

3. Which of the following pairs of words are most alike in meaning ?
   Invaluable—costly ; Cold—warm ; Necklace—diamonds.

4. Find the thing which is different in each line below :
   (a) Coat,   boots,   vest,   shirt,   socks.
   (b) Peas,   cabbage,   beans,   onions,   gravy.

5. The words of the following sentence have been mixed up. Think how the sentence should run and then write down whether it is *true* or *false.*
   in the Englishmen who protect sun hats live big to wear them from India.

6. By altering the position of two words the sentence below will be true. Which two words are they ?
   Some people eat their fingers with their food.

7. Why do we place flowers on the table ? Which is the best reason, (a), (b), (c) or (d) ?
   (a) To keep the air pure.
   (b) To make the table look nice.
   (c) To take away the smell of bad food.
   (d) To cover up dirty marks on the table.

8. John and James are brothers and they have their birthdays on the same day 14th May. They must be twins.
   What have you to say about this ?

9. Mary and Jane have bicycles.
   Elsie and Doris have skates.
   Mary and Elsie have scooters.
   (a) How many girls have each of the three things ?
   (b) How many girls have two of the three things ?
   (c) How many girls have only one of the three things ?

10. **Rose** is to **flower** as **dog** is to . . .
    Which of the following words would make the best ending to the above statement ?
    cat, animal, humans, scent

11. Write a single word which will do as a name for **ants, bees** and **wasps.**

12. Which figures are missing ?
    (a) 256,   128,   . . .,   32,   16.
    (b) 16,   16,   17,   . . .,   18,   18.

82

13. All **saucepans** have one of the following. Say which it is.

Lids, covers, handles, spouts.

14. A shopkeeper uses the words JOHN ALFRED as a code, so that J = 1, O = 2, H = 3, N = 4, A = 5, etc. He marks a chair OJ·EA. What do you think he will charge for it ?

15. *Make hay while the sun shines.*

Which statement is most like the above in meaning ?

(*a*) Make the most of your chances as they arise.

(*b*) If there is no sun leave the hay until another day.

(*c*) Enjoy yourself on sunny days.

16. If the following things were arranged in some sort of order, which would come in the middle ?

month, day, hour, week, year.

17. A square box has no lid. On how many surfaces outside could it be painted green ?

18. In a certain kind of secret writing CAT is written as DBU and DOG as EPH. How would MOUSE be spelt in the same secret writing ?

19. *Union is strength* means the same as one of the following. Which is it ?

(*a*) There can only be one master.

(*b*) If you join with others you will all increase your power.

(*c*) The strongest men are in the union.

20. Which two words are not needed if the following sentence is to make sense ?

England, Wales, Ireland and Scotland form the island continent of Great Britain.

21. Draw a triangle and then place a square on it so that one corner of the triangle is crossed by two lines of the square.

22. Find the two words in the list below which have opposite meanings :

heat, temperature, freezing, icy, melting

23. Which of the shapes numbered 1 to 4 is needed to make this ⌐ into a square ?

1   2   3   4

24. Look at the list of things below, and write down the one that is different in each line.

(*a*) Motor-bus, charabanc, bicycle, lorry.

(*b*) Pink, scarlet, crimson, violet, red.

(*c*) Jam, marmalade, fish-paste, honey, syrup.

TEST 20

1. One of these three words—**said, answered, asked**—can be used with the following mixed-up words to make a sensible sentence. Which word is it?

    Mother John some for his food.

2. Find two words in the next sentence which could be changed over in their position to make a sensible statement.

    Boys are not suitable toys for dolls.

3. Why do people carry about watches instead of clocks? Is it (*a*), (*b*), (*c*) or (*d*)?

    (*a*) Because they are nicer to look at.
    (*b*) Because they keep better time.
    (*c*) Because they are cheaper.
    (*d*) Because they are easier to carry.

4. Father fell ill yesterday morning and after two whole days he is no better.
    What would you think if you heard that said?

5. Jack can play the violin but not the piano.
    James can play the piano but not the flute.
    Joe can play the flute but not the violin.
    Harry can play the violin *and* the flute.

    If each boy can play two of the three instruments, which of them may be like Harry?

6.

    Draw the shape which is needed after the word *to* above.

7. What name can we give to things like **gold, silver, copper** and **tin,** but not **coal**?

8. Which two things among the following do all **bicycles** have?
    Lamps, wheels, rubber pedals, spokes, carriers.

9. Continue with two more letters each of the following rows:
    (*a*) M B I N B I O B I
    (*b*) A P O B O O C N O D M O

10. In what order do the following words come in a dictionary?
    consider, conflagration, connection, confound, content

11. **Book** is to **chapter** as **drama** is to:
    (*a*) Novel   (*b*) Play   (*c*) Act   (*d*) Actor   (*e*) Stage

12. The colours **red, orange, yellow, green, blue, indigo, mauve** and **purple** are put side by side into a circle divided into eight sections by lines running through the centre. What colour lies opposite **orange?**

13. Which letter comes half-way between G and S in the alphabet?

14. Find the two statements below which have opposite meanings :
 (a) He is sometimes a good workman.
 (b) Nothing that he does is ever satisfactory.
 (c) He likes to finish a job quickly.
 (d) His work has everything to recommend it.

15. Which pair of words are most alike in meaning ?
 oppose—assist ; prophesy—foretell ; order—forbid.

16. Write down the thing which is " different " in each of the following lists :
 (a) Ocean, river, lake, sea, sky.
 (b) Chair, table, couch, rug, stool.
 (c) Minute, hour, day, year, tomorrow.

17. Which two words in the following sentence ought to change places to make a sensible statement ?
 Fishermen spend much sea on the time.

18. Here are some words which have been mixed up. When they are put in the right order, do they make a *true* or a *false* statement ?
 Most petrol without go will motor cars.

19. Which is the best answer to this question : (a), (b), (c) or (d) ?
 Why don't iron ships sink ?
 (a) Because iron is lighter than water. (c) Because they are full of air.
 (b) Because iron is heavier than water. (d) Because they carry sails.

20. Jack jumped off the back of the bus and the front wheel passed over his foot. Could this really happen ? What do you think ?

21. Smith and Jones are fair.
 Brown and Robinson are dark.
 Smith and Robinson are tall.
 (a) who is tall and fair ?
 (b) who is tall and dark ?

22.
Finish the above by putting in the shape needed. It is one of the following :

23. Think in what way all the following are alike : **fragrance, odour, scent.** Which is the thing most like them among the following ?
 Nose, aroma, breeze, roses.

24. All **houses** have two of the following. Which are they ?
 Numbers, names, rooms, doors, gas stoves.

TEST 21

1. Add three more figures or letters to each of the following rows :
   (a) 8 9 0 7 8 0 6 7 0 . . .
   (b) O Z A O Y B O X C . . .

2. *When the cat's away the mice will play.*
   This means the same as one of the following. Which is it ?
   (a) Cats and mice do not agree.
   (b) When the person in charge is absent, those under him waste their time.
   (c) When the lion goes to sleep, the leopards wake up.

3. Dutchmen/Germans live in Holland/France and the Hindus/Chinese in Africa/India.
   Which four words must be omitted to leave a sensible statement ?

4. Arrange the following dates in their proper time-order :
   1894 A.D.,   1509 A.D.,   55 B.C.,   201 A.D.,   500 B.C.

5. If you face the south-west wind and put out your left hand sideways, in what direction will it point ?

6. One of the days of the week is spelt in " secret writing " as STDRCZX. How would you spell JUNE in the same secret writing ?

7. *A stitch in time saves nine.*
   This means the same as one of the following. Which is it ?
   (a) Nine o'clock is the best hour for sewing.
   (b) Things done at once may save you a good deal of time later on.
   (c) Sew with a regular movement ; for example, nine times a minute.

8. The farmer has to plough/sow his fields before/after he sows/raises his seeds/crops.
   Which four words must be omitted to leave a sensible statement ?

9. Draw two triangles partly across each other, making the shape like a diamond where they overlap.

10. Which two statements below have opposite meanings ?
    (a) The flowers are faded.
    (b) They have lost their petals.
    (c) The colour has gone out of them.
    (d) They have regained their former hue.

11. Which statements are most alike in meaning ?
    (a) Her arrival was unexpected.
    (b) Her homecoming was anxiously awaited.
    (c) She came without warning.

86

12. Which is the different thing in each of the following lists ?
    (a) 2, 4, 8, 32, 7, 16.
    (b) Italy, Germany, England, Paris, India.
    (c) Policeman, postman, visitor, chauffeur, teacher.

13. Which of these three words—**although, before, because**—could be used with the following mixture of words to make a true statement ?
    The down has gone dark is it sun.

14. Which two words can be changed over in position to make this statement true?
    Some boys are about while others play solitary in groups.

15. Why is night the best time for sleep ?
    What do you think is the correct answer : (a), (b), (c) or (d) ?
    (a) Because then the stars are out.
    (b) Because it is the quietest time to rest.
    (c) Because it is best to be out of doors in the daylight.
    (d) Because all the shops shut at night.

16. I remember the morning well because the daylight was just beginning to fade as I got out of bed.
    What would you think if the above statement were made in your hearing ?

17. The flowers were now at their best, particularly the roses.
    Which month, then, was it ?
    December, March, June, October.

18. Find the word needed to complete the following statement :
    Uncle is to **aunt** as **nephew** is to . . . which ?
    (Cousin, sister, niece, grandchild)

19. **Veil, shutter, screen.** Think in what way these things are alike. Now find the thing most like them among the following :
    Door, curtain, gate, gangway.

20. All **shadows** have one of the following. Which is it ?
    life, colour, form, substance

21. Add two more numbers to each of the sets of figures given below :
    (a) 16, 8, 4, 2, 1, $\frac{1}{2}$, . . .
    (b) 1, 2, 4, 7, 11, . . .

22. If the following were arranged in order of size, which would come in the middle ?
    town, village, continent, country, county

23. Can a triangle made of cardboard be cut in such a manner as to make two pieces, both of which are also triangles ? Name the right answer.
    Yes, No, You can't tell.

24. In a secret code the words SEE ME AT ONCE are written as VOO EO BY JQFO.
    What do you think the word YJE means ?

TEST 22

You are required to write (*a*), (*b*), (*c*), (*d*) or (*e*) for your answers **unless** you are told to do otherwise.

1. Write down the letter that occurs most often in CO-EXISTENCE.

2. The word most like TORMENT in meaning is :
   (*a*) Hit (*b*) Insult (*c*) Tease (*d*) Beat (*e*) Kick

3. Which figure would you say is opposite to A ?

    A   **B**   **C**   **D**   **E**

4. 81, 72, 63, 54. What number should come next ?
   (*a*) 43 (*b*) 44 (*c*) 45 (*d*) 46 (*e*) 47

5. **Forest** is to **Tree** as **Class** is to :
   (*a*) Pupil (*b*) Teacher (*c*) Desks (*d*) Lesson (*e*) School

6. What goes best with **pen, pencil, crayon ?**
   (*a*) Paper (*b*) Chalk (*c*) Paint (*d*) Rubber (*e*) Ink

7. Two words must change position to make sense in :
   The sunny was bright and evening
   Which are they ?

8. *Snow can usually be seen on mountain tops because* :
   (*a*) Mountain tops are near the sun.
   (*b*) It is colder on mountain tops than elsewhere.
   (*c*) The clouds protect the snow.
   (*d*) Mountain tops are usually bare.

9. I do not like oranges or apples. I have just bought some fruit. What do you think it is ? (*a*) Oranges (*b*) Apples (*c*) Both (*d*) Neither

10. In a certain code THURSDAY, P.M. is written 1 2 3 4 5 6 7 8 9 0.
    What does 2 3 4 4 8 — 3 9 mean in this code ?

11. Four children of the same family attend a school.
    Tom is in the class below John's.
    Mary is in the class above Sally's.
    Sally is in the class below Tom's.
    Who is in the highest class ?
    (*a*) Tom (*b*) John (*c*) Sally (*d*) Mary

12. Find the missing word in the following sentence :
    When you are . . . the time seems to pass quickly.
    (*a*) miserable (*b*) healthy (*c*) careful (*d*) happy (*e*) hurrying

13. Which letter in the word below comes *first* in the alphabet ?
    NINCOMPOOP

14. Choose the word most like COMBINE.
    (*a*) Mix (*b*) Collect (*c*) Arrange (*d*) Conclude (*e*) Harvest

15. Which shape would you say is the opposite of A ?

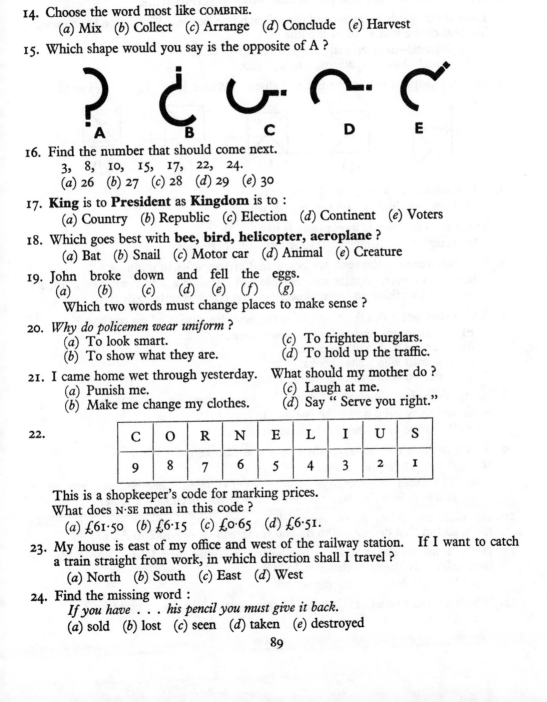

    A   B   C   D   E

16. Find the number that should come next.
    3, 8, 10, 15, 17, 22, 24.
    (*a*) 26 (*b*) 27 (*c*) 28 (*d*) 29 (*e*) 30

17. **King** is to **President** as **Kingdom** is to :
    (*a*) Country (*b*) Republic (*c*) Election (*d*) Continent (*e*) Voters

18. Which goes best with **bee, bird, helicopter, aeroplane** ?
    (*a*) Bat (*b*) Snail (*c*) Motor car (*d*) Animal (*e*) Creature

19. John broke down and fell the eggs.
    (*a*)   (*b*)   (*c*)   (*d*)   (*e*)   (*f*)   (*g*)
    Which two words must change places to make sense ?

20. *Why do policemen wear uniform ?*
    (*a*) To look smart.   (*c*) To frighten burglars.
    (*b*) To show what they are.   (*d*) To hold up the traffic.

21. I came home wet through yesterday. What should my mother do ?
    (*a*) Punish me.   (*c*) Laugh at me.
    (*b*) Make me change my clothes.   (*d*) Say " Serve you right."

22.

C	O	R	N	E	L	I	U	S
9	8	7	6	5	4	3	2	1

    This is a shopkeeper's code for marking prices.
    What does N·SE mean in this code ?
    (*a*) £61·50 (*b*) £6·15 (*c*) £0·65 (*d*) £6·51.

23. My house is east of my office and west of the railway station. If I want to catch
    a train straight from work, in which direction shall I travel ?
    (*a*) North (*b*) South (*c*) East (*d*) West

24. Find the missing word :
    If you have . . . his pencil you must give it back.
    (*a*) sold (*b*) lost (*c*) seen (*d*) taken (*e*) destroyed

TEST 23

1. Write down the letter that occurs most often in ELEPHANTINE.

2. Look at the words in the second part of each line below. Which one has a meaning like that of the first word in the line ?
   (a) *Gigantic*—mysterious, huge, strange, odd.
   (b) *Broad*—long, spacious, wide, big.

3. Find the shape which is like the first shape. Which is it : (a), (b), (c) or (d) ?

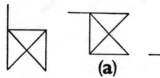 **(a)** **(b)** **(c)** **(d)**

4. All bicycles have what : (a), (b), (c) or (d) ?
   (a) bells (b) brakes (c) lamps (d) wheels

5. **Train** is to **station** as **aeroplane** is to :
   (a) Hangar (b) Runway (c) Airport (d) Terminus

6. Find two words in the sentence below that are opposite in meaning.
   Mary was clever, popular and sociable and attended a school where the teachers were hard working and sympathetic and no one was unfriendly.

7. Which sentence, (a), (b), (c) or (d), is the best description of **an author ?**
   (a) A person who writes for the newspapers.
   (b) A person who makes up stories.
   (c) A person who writes books.
   (d) A person who prints books and magazines.

8. In the following sentence the words have got mixed up. Put them in the right order and then write down the last word.
   fire the goose of mother in the roasted front.

9. Why was there no television when your grandfather was a boy ?
   Write down (a), (b), (c) or (d).
   (a) There was no electricity.   (c) " Wireless " had not been invented.
   (b) It was before the war.   (d) It had been kept a secret.

10. Six children—John, Mary, Ann, Philip, Tom and Jean—sit round a circular table, and in that order. Who do you think will sit opposite to Ann ?

11. Harry is not so clever as Peter but he is less stupid than John. Eric is cleverer than John. Is Harry as clever as John ?
    (a) Yes (b) No (c) One cannot tell.

12. Which are the two letters that should come next in the following series ?
    B C A B B B C A B B

13. The following word is used as a code so that instead of letters, figures are used.
    S E C O N D A R Y
    1 2 3 4 5 6 7 8 9
    How would you write ROSY in figures ?

14. *Copper costs more than iron.*
    Find two statements below that make this true.
    (a) Lead is more costly than iron. (c) Copper is more costly than lead.
    (b) Silver is more costly than lead. (d) Copper is less costly than silver.

15. PARALLELOGRAM. How many letters in this word occur more than once ?

16. In the sentence below there are two words opposite in meaning. Which are they?
    Though many competitors will take part in the struggle, few will succeed.

17. In the next sentence find two words that have almost the same meaning.
    The outlook was a gloomy one but the explorers continued to climb for there
    was, at least, the prospect of a rest ahead.

18. When the following words have been put into sensible order, one more word will
    be needed to complete the sentence. What is it ?
    one one make pence hundred.

19. All elephants have what : (a), (b), (c) or (d) ?
    (a) Manes (b) Fleece (c) Hides (d) Horns

20. **Lantern** is to **light** as **fire** is to . . .
    (a) Heat (b) Ashes (c) Smoke (d) Flames

21.
G	R	A	C	I	O	U	S	L	Y
1	2	3	4	5	6	7	8	9	0

Using the above code, what do you think is the meaning of the following message ?
    4 3 2 1 6 — 5 8 — 6 7 2 8

22. *Dick can run faster than Tom.*
    Which two statements below make the above statement true ?
    (a) Dick can run as fast as Will. (c) Will is the champion runner.
    (b) Dick ran run farther than Will. (d) Will can run faster than Tom.

23. Which two letters ought to come next in this series ?
    A B C B C A C A B

24. Which shape, (a), (b), (c) or (d), is like A ?

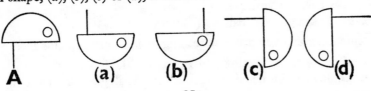

91

TEST 24

1. **Queen** is to **Kingdom** as **President** is to :
    (*a*) America (*b*) Republic (*c*) State (*d*) Country

2. Which number below occurs more than once ?
    67123 67213 62173 67132
    67231 67132 62371 67223

3. Write down the letters of the word ORANGE in the order in which they come in the alphabet.

4. Find the odd one among the following :
    Crab, Lobster, Tortoise, Turtle, Frog.

5. Tom had fewer sums right than John.
    John had fewer sums right than Eric.
    Who had the most right answers ?

6. My summer holiday starts in six days' time. Yesterday it was my birthday—Friday, June 23rd. On which day of the week will my holiday start ?

7. Find two words in the line below that are opposite in meaning :
    Careful, needful, negligent, thoughtful, sulky.

8. Write down the letter that comes just before the fifth letter after M in the alphabet.

9. *Half a loaf is better than no bread*,
    means—(*a*), (*b*), (*c*) or (*d*) ?
    (*a*) A whole loaf is too much for anyone.
    (*b*) The first half of a loaf is always the best.
    (*c*) A little of anything good is better than nothing at all.
    (*d*) Don't be greedy.

10.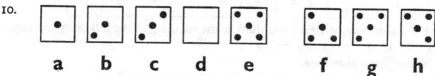
       a   **b**   **c**   **d**   **e**   **f**   **g**   **h**

    Which square, (*f*), (*g*) or (*h*), would you place where (*d*) is ?

11. Four children sit in a row in this order :
    John, Mary, Eric and Ann. John then changes places with Eric and then Eric changes places with Mary.
    In what order do they sit now ?

12. **Rivers** always have—what ?
    (*a*) boats (*b*) bridges (*c*) banks (*d*) tides

13. In this sentence which you are now reading which word contains most letter E's ?

14. Find a word opposite in meaning to AWKWARD in the following :
    John was clumsy in his dancing : in fact, not at all graceful in anything he did.

15.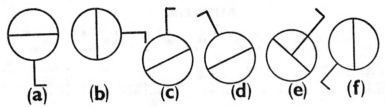

Which two of the above figures are the same in shape ?

16. Say which word goes best with **Alan, Tom** and **John**.

Joan, name, boys, brothers, Eric.

17.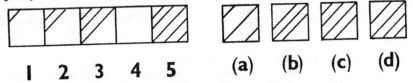

Which shape on the right should be placed in No. 4 ?

18. Arm is to **hand** as **leg** is to—which ?

body, toe, ankle, sole, foot

19. Which *two* of the following does a room *always* have ?

Furniture, Lino, Floor, Fireplace, Walls

20. Why does a regiment of soldiers have its own special flag ? Which do you think is the best of the reasons below ?

(*a*) To make a good impression when marching.
(*b*) To add colour and cheerfulness to the regiment.
(*c*) To show the soldiers where their comrades are gathered.
(*d*) To lead the way.

21. Meg is a dancer. Nearly all dancers are graceful. Is Meg graceful ?

Yes, No, Cannot say.

22. Firemen wear helmets at fires. The Life Guards wear helmets on parade. Mr. Henry is a fireman. Does he wear a helmet on parade ?

Yes, No, Cannot tell.

23. Lead is heavier than silver. Silver is lighter than copper. Which is the lightest ?

Lead, Silver, Copper, Cannot tell.

24.

L	I	F	E	B	O	A	T	S
1	2	3	4	5	6	7	8	9

Using the above as a code, what do you think this means ?

28—29—9734—86—9411—711—56689

ANSWERS

Exercise 1a. 1. E   2. S   3. V   4. D   5. C   6. I   7. I   8. L   9. W   10. M, N   11. O   12. E   13. I   14. U   15. S   16. November   17. S   18. Yam   19. Wednesday   20. August   21. 3   22. 15   23. 16   24. R   25. 7   26. 27   27. 24   28. 20   29. fifteen   30. 3281.

Exercise 2a. 1. big   2. feeble   3. moist   4. expensive   5. governor   6. rich   7. approaching   8. acute   9. frequently   10. combat   11. mighty   12. corridor   13. strange   14. lasting   15. brave   16. detest   17. frighten   18. obscure   19. good-natured   20. subtract   21. thankfulness   22. zeal   23. distress   24. approval   25. grace   26. forbearance   27. waste   28. caution   29. astonishment   30. character.

Exercise 2b. 1. transparent   2. correct   3. sad   4. considerable   5. brittle   6. importance   7. unable to read   8. yearly   9. shorten   10. stupidity.

Exercise 2c. 1. (3)   2. (2)   3. (3)   4. (1)   5. (3).

Exercise 2d. 1. (b)   2. (a)   3. (d)   4. (c).

Exercise 3a. 1. below   2. thin   3. blunt   4. far   5. sinner   6. strong   7. rough   8. lead   9. forget   10. war.

Exercise 3b. 1. gentle, violent   2. destroy, construct   3. innocent, guilty   4. give, receive   5. exit, entrance   6. important, insignificant   7. costly, inexpensive   8. energetic, lazy   9. display, conceal   10. diminish, increase.

Exercise 3c. 1. (3)   2. (2)   3. (3)   4. (1)   5. (3)   6. (4)   7. (1)   8. (2)   9. (1)   10. (3).

Exercise 3d. 1. O   2. O   3. S   4. S   5. S   6. N   7. N   8. O   9. S   10. N.

Exercise 3e. 1. O retreat   2. S answer   3. O simple   4. O opaque   5. O collect   6. S belief   7. S accompany   8. S prominent   9. S save   10. S persist.

Exercise 3f. 1. carelessly   2. invited   3. reluctantly   4. plainly   5. hopelessly.

Exercise 3g. 1. 4   2. 3   3. 3   4. 2   5. 4   6. 2   7. 2   8. 2   9. 4   10. 2.

Exercise 4a. 1. tulip   2. umbrella   3. paper   4. sit   5. earth   6. table   7. lard   8. square   9. potato   10. engine   11. crab   12. turkey   13. handkerchief   14. farmer   15. bugler   16. Paris   17. brandy   18. tomatoes   19. ass   20. 2.

Exercise 4b. 1. electrician   2. steamer   3. IX   4. padre   5. flat   6. copper   7. waterfall   8. assembly   9. clan   10. solder   11. intelligent   12. next year   13. contentment   14. pursue   15. handsome   16. occupation   17. geography   18. obstruct   19. spill   20. repeatedly.

Exercise 4c. 1. (3)   2. (2)   3. (3)   4. (1)   5. (3)   6. (3)   7. (4)   8. (4)   9. (1)   10. (2).

Exercise 5a. 1. 13, 15   2. 20, 23   3. 22, 29   4. 49, 64   5. 8, 7   6. 2, 1   7. 68, 64   8. 37, 42   9. 6, 4   10. 5, 4   11. 9, 3   12. 105, 120   13. $\frac{1}{2}, \frac{1}{4}$ 14. 33, 22   15. 607, 708   16. $\frac{3}{20}, \frac{5}{23}$ 17. 8, 9   18. 25, 29   19. $\frac{1}{4}, \frac{1}{16}$ 20. 576, 687.

Exercise 5b. 1. 10   2. 20   3. 71   4. 0   5. 14   6. 30   7. 8   8. 8 or $\frac{8}{8}$ 9. 60   10. 126.

Exercise 5c. 1. 6   2. 27   3. 18   4. 4   5. 16   6. 21   7. 3   8. 16   9. 406   10. $2\frac{1}{4}$.

Exercise 5d. 1. A, B   2. A, G   3. g, d   4. d, v   5. q, m   6. u, v   7. u, x   8. o, u   9. v, q   10. c, d.

Exercise 6a. 1. salt   2. bird   3. snow or ice   4. run   5. night   6. hand   7. girls   8. bad   9. carpenter (joiner)   10. book   11. cart   12. slow   13. pencil   14. air   15. forest.

Exercise 6b. 1. narrow   2. water   3. spade   4. cry   5. soldiers   6. tool   7. night   8. steel   9. spending   10. creeping.

Exercise 6c. 1. age   2. painting   3. honey   4. lake   5. daughter   6. motor car   7. liquid   8. floor   9. climb   10. aeroplane.

Exercise 6d. 1. carpenter, furniture   2. water, steam   3. miner, pickaxe   4. speech, hear   5. polite, well-mannered   6. paddle, bathe   7. Thomas, Elizabeth   8. long, length   9. pleasure, laugh   10. home, family.

Exercise 6e. 1. HI   2. there   3. 81   4. woman   5. constellation   6. mother   7. come   8. beef   9. distance   10. nowhere.

Exercise 6f. 1. 7   2. 5   3. 6   4. 6   5. 7.

Exercise 6g. 1. 6   2. 7   3. 5   4. 7.

Exercise 7a. 1. horse   2. shark   3. eagle   4. hare   5. horse   6. turtle   7. elephant   8. badger   9. cow   10. turkey.

Exercise 7b. 1. marble   2. daisy   3. plum   4. $\frac{1}{2}$p   5. cottage   6. flute   7. eye   8. bullet   9. meteor   10. leaf.

Exercise 7c. 1. youth   2. town   3. lake   4. chest   5. hour   6. page   7. waistcoat   8. house   9. France   10. yacht.

Exercise 7d. 1. large   2. sometimes   3. naughty   4. interested   5. friendly   6. grey   7. warm   8. some   9. good   10. quick.

Exercise 7e. 1. minim (4)   2. slap (4)   3. stroll (2)   4. November (5)   5. deafening (5)   6. trio (3)   7. scarlet (4)   8. south-east (4)   9. perpetual (5)   10. despatch case (2).

Exercise 7f. 1. 5   2. 3   3. 4   4. 1   5. 2.

Exercise 8a. 1. carrots, donkeys   2. milk, Mary   3. east, sun   4. room, bed   5. say, what   6. hat, did   7. Maud, into   8. all, have   9. kettle, mother   10. than, colder.

Exercise 8b. 1. F 2. T 3. T 4. F 5. T 6. F 7. F 8. T 9. F 10. F.

Exercise 8c. 1. cold 2. ill 3. women 4. morning (day) 5. year 6. water 7. steam 8. shortest 9. write 10. hands (fingers).

Exercise 8d. 1. summer (appear) 2. up 3. days 4. wall 5. ice-cream 6. socks 7. England 8. trusted 9. warmth 10. John.

Exercise 8e. 1. salt 2. equator 3. school 4. barrier 5. team 6. collision 7. success 8. present 9. house 10. lost.

Exercise 9a. 1. *(b)* 2. *(d)* 3. *(a)* 4. *(c)* 5. *(d)* 6. *(c)* 7. *(a)* 8. *(b)* 9. *(c)* 10. *(b)* 11. *(c)* 12. *(c)*.

Exercise 10a. 1. Mark 2. Paul 3. Snowdrops 4. Tim 5. Molly 6. Jack 7. 850 g 8. 72 9. December 28th, 1969 10. Grape 11. *(a)* 10 *(b)* 30 *(c)* 25 *(d)* 25 *(e)* 25 12. *(a)* April 26th *(b)* May 1st *(c)* May 3rd *(d)* Wednesday *(e)* 5 13. *(a)* 103 *(b)* Saturday *(c)* 34 *(d)* rings *(e)* Monday 14. *(a)* Peter *(b)* David *(c)* John, David *(d)* Ann *(e)* Peter 15. *(a)* Tim *(b)* Tom *(c)* Terry *(d)* Terry *(e)* Tim, Ted.

Exercise 11a. 1. *(a) (c)* 2. *(a) (d)* 3. *(a) (c)* 4. *(b) (d)* 5. *(a) (d)* 6. *(a) (c)* 7. *(a) (b)* 8. *(c) (d)* 9. *(a) (d)* 10. *(a) (d)*.

Exercise 11b. 1. *(d)* 2. *(c)* 3. *(b)* 4. *(a)* 5. *(e)* 6. *(c)* 7. *(a)* 8. *(b)* 9. *(b)* 10. *(c)* 11. *(b)*.

Exercise 12a. 1. J 2. H 3. F 4. 10 5. £41·06 6. £10·60 7. E·DJ 8. IEJ·JJ 9. HB·CE 10. Hide dead chief.

Exercise 12b. 1. flag 2. stop 3. war 4. cake 5. ink 6. wit 7. wolf 8. gzyov 9. street 10. hvv.

Exercise 12c. 1. fmxov 2. zfmgrv 3. xlfhrm 4. nlgsvi 5. urg zmw dvoo 6. niy 7. rswf 8. pihs 9. qfosr 10. eiffia.

Exercise 12d. 1. November 2. QIIX QI ERC XMQI 3. Can't you be quiet? 4. £3·69 5. £58·42 6. A·MA 7. TE·LA 8. ZXE ZU LOTJ SGXE LUX AY 9. Tuesday 10. GVXOR GTJ SGE.

Exercise 13a. 1. green 2. less 3. plane 4. knock 5. blots 6. longest 7. expand 8. freeze 9. dry 10. starch.

Exercise 13b. 1. red, yellow 2. fearless, timid 3. hungry, meal 4. work, finish 5. shoes, knot 6. stamp, post 7. think, yourself 8. lightning, thunder 9. bread, build 10. early, finish.

Exercise 13c. 1. strange 2. way 3. do 4. policeman 5. him 6. staying 7. how 8. certainly 9. first 10. before.

Exercise 13d. 1. coal 2. substances 3. fields 4. medicines 5. radio 6. heal 7. tar 8. petrol 9. substituted 10. explosives.

Exercise 14a. 1. *(3)* 2. *(4)* 3. *(2)* 4. *(4)* 5. *(2)* 6. *(1)* 7. *(4)* 8. *(2)* 9. *(4)* 10. *(3)*.

Exercise 14b. 1. *(3)* 2. *(4)* 3. *(1)* 4. *(3)* 5. *(4)* 6. *(4)* 7. *(4)* 8. *(1)* 9. *(2)* 10. *(3)*.

Exercise 14c. 1. *(2)* 2. *(1)* 3. *(4)* 4. *(4)* 5. *(3)* 6. *(3)* 7. *(3)* 8. *(1)* 9. *(3)* 10. *(4)*.

Test 1. 1. R 2. huge 3. come 4. ticket 5. I 6. IX 7. head 8. sing 9. *(3)* 10. Tuesday, May 25th 11. £7·68 12. eggs 13. two 14. *(b)* 15. weak 16. *(4)* 17. 3 18. April 20th 19. *(2)* 20. hammer, man 21. *(d)* 22. *(c)* 23. walls 24. 16.

Test 2. 1. *(2)* 2. *(3)* 3. *(3)* 4. *(4)* 5. *(5)* 6. *(4)* 7. *(1)* 8. *(4)* 9. *(4)* 10. *(2)* 11. *(4)* 12. *(2)* 13. *(2)* 14. *(3)* 15. *(3)* 16. *(1)* 17. *(5)* 18. *(4)* 19. *(4)* 20. *(2)* and *(7)* 21. *(3)* 22. *(2)* 23. *(3)* 24. *(2)*.

Test 3. 1. nine not 9 2. determined 3. spend 4. carpenter 5. 13 6. hip 7. *(4)* 8. b 9. *(a)* 10. Jack 11. soles 12. 6 hours 13. fish 14. 8 15. paragraph 16. 1, 5 17. Winter 18. *(c)* 19. 90 20. height 21. GEXGL XLI ETI 22. 4 23. 2 24. *(1)* and *(4)*

Test 4. 1. *(3)* 2. *(2)* 3. *(4)* 4. *(4)* 5. *(4)* 6. *(3)* 7. *(2)* 8. *(2)* 9. *(2)* 10. *(4)* 11. *(1)* 12. *(3)* 13. *(2)* 14. *(4)* 15. *(3)* 16. *(2)* 17. *(3)* 18. *(3)* 19. *(3)* 20. *(1)* 21. *(4)* 22. *(1)* and *(2)* 23. *(4)* 24. *(5)*.

Test 5. 1. *(3)* dwelling 2. *(3)* H 3. *(3)* today 4. *(3)* time 5. *(3)* reach 6. *(4)* 7. *(5)* 11 8. *(2)* 9. *(2)* sleeves 10. *(2)* 21 11. *(2)* outstanding 12. *(3)* thick skinned 13. *(5)* 30 14. *(5)* oil lamp 15. *(1)* yesterday 16. *(2)* instruments 17. *(4)* 18. *(3)* 19. *(1)* true 20. *(1)* John 21. seldom 22. 18 23. enthusiastic 24. disgust.

Test 6. 1. Ache 2. *(4)* put in 3. *(2)* strange 4. *(4)* niece 5. 37 6. *(1)* measles 7. *(4)* 8. *(1)* handles 9. *(1)* Yes 10. *(1)* north-east 11. *(2)* nut 12. *(2)* Dick 13. *(4)* right angle 14. *(3)* No. 24 15. *(1)* 16. *(3)* lard 17. *(2)* o o 18. *(3)* Whitsuntide 19. *(2)* pedal 20. *(4)* 21. *(3)* 22. *(1)* ices 23. *(1)* and *(3)* 24. *(3)* £1·00.

Test 7. 1. No 2. impolite 3. graceful, elegant 4. twig 5. down-pour 6. 16, 32 7. ½ 8. heat 9. *(c)* 10. *(d)* 11. P.UH 12. December 13. You can't tell 14. 31 15. sergeant 16. *(2)* 17. mother 18. *(a)* 19. tall, darker 20. shape 21. FILE or LIEF 22. *(c)* 23. approving 24. acquire.

Test 8. 1. *(3)* 2. *(2)* 3. *(1)* and *(4)* 4. *(2)* 5. *(1)* 6. *(2)* 7. *(4)* 8. *(5)* 9. *(4)* 10. *(3)* 11. *(2)* 12. *(4)* 13. *(1)* 14. *(4)* 15. *(2)* 16. *(2)* 17. *(1)* and *(4)* 18. *(5)* 19. *(3)* 20. *(2)* 21. *(4)* 22. *(2)* 23. *(3)* 24. *(3)*.

Test 9. 1. *(c)* 2. *(a)* and *(d)* 3. *(5)* 4. *(4)* 5. *(3)* 6. *(2)* 7. *(d)* 8. *(b)* 9. *(1)* 10. *(4)* 11. *(3)* 12. *(e)* 13. *(a)* 14. *(4)* 15. *(3)* 16. *(c)* 17. *(4)* 18. *(3)* 19. *(d)* 20. *(2)* 21. *(2)* 22. *(4)* 23. *(e)* 24. *(b)*.

Test 10. 1. child 2. GO 3. house 4. *(1)* 5. P 6. *(b)* 7. true 8. out 9. catch 10. SELUCREH 11. *(b)* 12. mean 13. R 14. never 15. rarely 16. potato 17. school or books 18. Absurd— 19. *(c)* 20. inventions, every year 21. Bath 22. above 23. minerals 24. stems.

95

Test 11. 1. 22, 29   2. January 4th   3. average   4. line, angle, triangle, oblong   6. They see me   7. (a)
8. although   9. ON   10. similar   11. warmth   12. shoes   13. the sour apples gave the greedy boy a pain
14. ill   15. (c)   16. (d)   17. gold is heavier than lead   18. getting up   19. vehicles   20. handles
21. 36, 49   22. (a) and (c)   23. I went to the stationer's to buy father some ink   24. ZRRG ZR NG GRA.

Test 12. 1. (4)   2. (3)   3. (1)   4. (3)   5. (2)   6. (3)   7. (2)   8. (4)   9. (2)   10. (2)
11. (2)   12. (2)   13. (4)   14. (3)   15. (4)   16. (1)   17. (3)   18. (c)   19. (7)   20. (3)
21. (d)   22. (4)   23. (c)   24. (c).

Test 13. 1. net, ten   2. placid   3. sorrow   4. ink   5. false   6. luxuries to necessities   7. (c)
8. myself . . .   9. can't tell   10. (d)   11. (a) metals   (b) vegetables   12. (a) mouths   (b) goods
13. 1, 6   14. street   15. 3   16. CZMFDQ   17. (c)   18. unfortunately   19. (a) and (b)
20. Girls can usually sew better than boys   21. M   22. pride   23. receive   24. rice.

Test 14. 1. false   2. (a) wall, stone   (b) street, penny   3. (d)   5. 3   6. (c)   7. living things
8. (a) banks, water   (b) houses, streets   9. 31, 32   10. dog   12. what are two fours ?   13. (a) No
14. work   15. (a) aromatic   (b) manufactured   16. (a) goat   (b) orange   17. true   18. (a) handles, buckets
(b) children, flowers   19. to be easily recognized   20. Each must have one less brother/sister than the other   21. silk
22. enemies   23. all made of rubber   24. floors.

Test 15. 1. 37, 50   2. (b)   3. fly, nowhere, horseback   4. youth   5. south-west   6. Qlsm szh ivgfimvw
7. (c)   8. in case, lest   9. (a) 2   (b) 5   10. ancient, up-to-date   11. (a) gigantic   (b) pitiful   12. London, Paris
13. (a) sea   (b) spoons   14. (a) head, nail   (b) not, have   (c) hear, saw   15. (b)   17. (a) nephew   (b) can't
tell   18. wrist   19. blood relations   20. a door   21. 26, 37   22. A = 20, E = 17, I = 9, O = 6, U = 6
23. hour   24. Diamond is in the vase by the stable.

Test 16. 1. (a) 1   (b) 6   2. often   3. leopard   4. table   5. (a) false   (b) true   6. (a) baby, egg
(b) little, sticky   (c) is, spend   7. (b)   9. neither   10. lesson   11. (a) means of transport   (b) all plants
12. (a) bones   (b) seats   13. (a) 51, 39   (b) 5, 7   14. all used twice   15. warm   16. £1·56   17. (a)
18. cellar, coal   19. (c)   20. although   21. (a) seventeen   (b) E   22. clever, stupid   23. unhappy
24. diagram.

Test 17. 1. It is unsafe to drink dirty water   2. (a) hot, in   (b) ground, roots   3. (d)   4. only three people
5. Jack   6. (a) head   (b) peas   7. (a) senses   (b) precious stones   8. (a) roots   (b) tongues   9. page
10. B E D   11. GHIPRTU   12. Are you ready ?   13. T(hursday), S(aturday)   14. (a) different   (b) thawed
15. renovate   16. (a) cucumber   (b) teacher   (c) water   17. fish, went   18. wood   19. (b)   21. (a) Dick
(b) John   22. cold   23. peat   24. handles.

Test 18. 1. (a) 3   (b) 25   2. apple, banana, bread, cheese, peach, plum   3. 12.30   4. £25·15   5. (d)
6. since   7. L   8. unsatisfactory   9. (a) and (c)   10. (a) fruit   (b) a virtue   11. organs, musicians
12. true   13. (c)   15. (a) You cannot tell   (b) No   16. (a) foot, shoe   (b) fish, bird   17. agile   18. retreat
19. bed   20. legs   21. (a) 5   (b) 2   22. steam engine   23. rough   24. NLOOB.

Test 19. 1. K   2. distinct, vague   3. invaluable, costly   4. (a) boots   (b) gravy   5. true   6. fingers, food
7. (a)   8. not necessarily   9. (a) none   (b) two   (c) two   10. animal   11. insect   12. (a) 64   (b) 1
13. handles   14. £21·95   15. (a)   16. week   17. 5   18. NPVTF   19. (b)   20. Ireland,
continent   22. freezing, melting   23. 3   24. (a) bicycle   (b) violet   (c) fish-paste.

Test 20. 1. asked   2. boys, dolls   3. (d)   7. Jack   7. metal   8. wheels, spokes   9. (a) P B
(b) E L   10. conflagration, confound, connection, consider, content   11. act   12. indigo   13. M
14. (b) and (d)   15. prophesy, foretell   16. (a) sky   (b) rug   (c) tomorrow   17. sea, time   18. false
19. (c)   20. No   21. (a) Smith   (b) Robinson   22. (a)   23. aroma   24. rooms, doors.

Test 21. 1. (a) 5 6 0   (b) O W D   2. (b)   3. Germans, France, Chinese, Africa   4. 500 B.C. 55 B.C.
201 A.D. 1509 A.D. 1894 A.D.   5. South-east   6. ITMD   7. (b)   8. sow, after, raises, crops   10. (a) and (d)
11. (a) and (c)   12. (a) 7   (b) Paris   (c) visitor   13. because   14. about, solitary   15. (b)   17. June
18. niece   19. curtain   20. form   21. (a) ½, ½   (b) 16, 22   22. county   23. Yes   24. Tom.

Test 22. 1. (e)   2. (c)   3. (b)   4. (c)   5. (a)   6. (b)   7. sunny, evening   8. (b)   9. (d)
10. Hurry up   11. (b)   12. (d)   13. (c)   14. (a)   15. (c)   16. (b)   17. (b)   18. (a)
19. (b) and (e)   20. (b)   21. (b)   22. (b) and (c)   23. (c)   24. (d).

Test 23. 1. E   2. (a) huge   (b) wide   3. (d)   4. wheels   5. airport   6. sociable, unfriendly
7. (c)   8. fire   9. (c)   10. Jean   11. (a)   12. CA   13. 8419   14. (a) and (c)   15. Three : ARL
16. many, few   17. outlook, prospect   18. POUND   19. (c)   20. heat   21. cargo is ours
22. (a) and (d)   23. AB   24. (c).

Test 24. 1. (b) Republic   2. 67132   3. AEGNOR   4. frog   5. Eric   6. Friday   7. careful,
negligent   8. Q   9. (c)   10. (g)   11. Mary, Eric, John, Ann   12. banks   13. sentence
14. graceful   15. (a) and (d)   16. Eric   17. (a)   18. foot   19. floor, walls   20. (c)   21. cannot
say   22. cannot tell   23. silver   24. It is safe to sell all boots.